Science and the
Common Understanding

J. ROBERT OPPENHEIMER

Simon and Schuster
New York

Library of Congress Catalog Card Number: 54–8650
Dewey Decimal Classification Number: 530.1

CONTENTS

Science and the
Common Understanding

1.

NEWTON:

THE PATH OF LIGHT

SCIENCE has changed the conditions of man's life. It has changed its material conditions; by changing them it has altered our labor and our rest, our power, and the limits of that power, as men and as communities of men, the means and instruments as well as the substance of our learning, the terms and the form in which decisions of right and wrong come before us. It has altered the communities in which we live and cherish, learn and act. It has brought an acute and pervasive sense of change itself into our own life's span. The ideas of science have changed the way men think of themselves and of the world.

The description of these changes is not simple; it is rich in opportunity for error. As for the great material changes which science and practical art have made possible—machines, for instance, or power, the preservation of life, the urbanization of populations, new instruments of war, new means of communication and information—these are but part of the materials for the analysis of political economy and the wisdom and the insight of history. These are strands in the tangled affairs of men, and their evaluation is no more likely to be final and exhaustive than in any other part of history.

As for the more direct effects of discovery in science on the way men think about things which are not themselves part of science, the historian of ideas has a similar problem. Noting what in actual fact men have said about what they thought, who it was that thought it, and why he thought it, one finds, as in all history, that the contingent and the unpredictable, the peculiar greatnesses and blindnesses of individual men play a determining part. One even finds the science of great scientists taken in the name of those scientists for views and attitudes wholly foreign and sometimes wholly repugnant to them. Both Einstein and Newton created syntheses and insight so compelling and so grand that they induced in professional philosophers a great stir of not always convenient readjustment. Yet the belief in physical progress, the bright gaiety, and the relative indifference to religion characteristic of the enlightenment, were as foreign to Newton's character and preoccupation as could be; this did not keep the men of the enlightenment from regarding Newton as their patron and prophet. The philosophers and popularizers who have mistaken relativity for the doctrine of relativism have construed Einstein's great works as reducing the objectivity, firmness, and consonance to law of the physical world, whereas it is clear that Einstein has seen in his theories of relativity only a further confirmation of Spinoza's view that it is man's highest function to know and to understand the objective world and its laws.

Often the very fact that the words of science are the same as those of our common life and tongue can be more misleading than enlightening, more frustrating to understanding than recognizably technical jargon. For the words of science—relativity, if you will, or atom, or mutation, or action—have been given a refinement, a precision, and in the end a wholly altered meaning.

Thus we may well be cautious if we inquire as to whether there are direct connections, and if so of what sort, between the truths that science uncovers and the way men think about things in general—their metaphysics—their ideas about what is real and what is primary; their epistemology—their understanding of what makes human knowledge; their ethics—their ways of thinking, talking, judging, and acting in human problems of right and wrong, of good and evil.

These relations, the relations between scientific findings and man's general views, are indeed deep, intimate, and subtle. If I did not believe that, I should hardly be addressing these lectures to an attempt to elucidate what there is new in atomic physics that is relevant, helpful, and inspiring for men to know; but the relations are not, I think, relations of logical necessity. This is because science itself is, if not an unmetaphysical, at least a non-metaphysical activity. It takes common sense for granted as well as most of what has gone before in the specialized sciences. And where it adds, alters, or upsets, it does so on the basis of an uncritical acceptance of a great deal else. Thus, to the irritation of many, the assertions of science tend to keep away from the use of words like "real" and "ultimate." The special circumstances of the discovery of scientific truth are never very far from our minds when we expound it, and they act as a protecting sheath against their unlimited and universal acceptance. A few illustrations may make this clearer.

We have discovered atoms. In many ways they act like the atoms of the atomists. They are the stuff of which matter is made; their constellation and motion account for much—in fact, for most of the ordinarily observable properties of matter. But neither they nor the smaller, less composite particles of which they are made are either permanent, unchanging, or unchangeable. They do not act like objects of fixed form and infinite hardness. Such findings may be persuasive in discouraging the view that the world is made of fixed, immutable, infinitely hard little spheres and other shapes; but such findings are not in the nature of things conclusive, for one may always hold that the true atoms, the immutable, hard atoms, have so far eluded physical discovery, but that they are nevertheless there, and only when they are found will physics be dealing with the ultimate reality. Beyond that, one can hold that, although they may never be found by physical experiment, they are the underlying reality in terms of which all else, including the world of physics, is to be understood.

Or, again, we may have discovered that as the nervous impulses pass from the retina of the eye toward the brain itself their geometric disposition resembles less and less that of the object seen. This may complicate or qualify the view that the idea is a geometric replica of the object of vision. It cannot and need not wholly exorcise it.

The scientist may be aware that, whatever his findings, and indeed whatever his field of study, his search for truth is based on communication with other people, on agreement as to results of observation and experiment, and on talking in a common tongue about the instruments and apparatus and objects and procedures which he and others use. He may be aware of the fact that he has learned almost everything he knows from the books and the deeds and talk of other people; and, in so far as these experiences are vivid to him and he is a thoughtful man, he may be hesitant to think that only his own consciousness is real and all else illusion. But that view, too, is not by logic exorcised; from time to time it may rule his spirit.

Although any science gives countless examples of the interrelation of general law and changing phenomena, and although the progress of science has much to do with the enrichment of these relations, knowledge of science and practice of it and interest in it neither compel nor deny the belief that the changing phenomena of the actual world are illusion, that only the unchanging and permanent ideas are real.

If, in the atomic world, we have learned—as we have learned—that events are not causally determined by a strict, efficient, or formal cause; if we have learned to live with this and yet to recognize that for all of the common experience with ordinary bodies and ordinary happenings this atomic lack of causality is of no consequence and no moment, neither the one finding nor the other ensures that men when they think of the world at large are bound to a causal or a non-causal way of thinking.

These many examples show that there can indeed be conflict between the findings of science and what a philosopher or a school of philosophy has said in great particular about some part of experience now accessible to science. But they also show that, if there are relationships between what the sciences reveal about the world and how men think about those parts of it either not yet or never to be explored by science, these are not relationships of logical necessity; they are not relationships which are absolute and compelling, and they are not of such a character that the unity and coherence of an intellectual community can be based wholly upon it.

But if these examples indicate, as we should indeed expect from the nature and conditions of scientific inquiry, that what science finds does not and cannot uniquely determine what men think of as real and as important, they must show as well that there is a kind of relevance—a relevance which will appear different to different men and which will be responsive to many influences outside the work of science. This relevance is a kind of analogy, often of great depth and scope, in which views which have been created or substantiated in some scientific enterprise are similar to those which might be held with regard to metaphysical, epistemological, political, or ethical problems. The success of a critical and sceptical approach in science may encourage a sceptical approach in politics or in ethics; the discovery of an immensely successful theory of great scope may encourage the quest for a simplified view of human institutions. The example of rapid progress in understanding may lead men to conclude that the root of evil is ignorance and that ignorance can be ended.

All these things have happened and all surely will happen again. This means that, if we are to take heart from any beneficent influence that science may have for the common understanding, we need to do so both with modesty and with a full awareness that these relationships are not inevitably and inexorably for man's good.

It is my thesis that generally the new things we have learned in science, and specifically what we have learned in atomic physics, do provide us with valid and relevant and greatly needed analogies to human problems lying outside the present domain of science or its present borderlands. Before I talk of what is new I shall need to sketch, with perhaps an exaggerated simplicity and contrast, the state of knowledge and belief to which these correctives may apply. In doing this, we may have in mind that the general notions about human understanding and community which are illustrated by discoveries in atomic physics are not in the nature of things wholly unfamiliar, wholly unheard of, or new. Even in our own culture they have a history, and in Buddhist and Hindu thought a more considerable and central place. What we shall find is an exemplification, an encouragement, and a refinement of old wisdom. We shall not need to debate whether, so altered, it is old or new.

There are, then, two sketches that I would like to draw of the background for the altered experience of this century. One is the picture of the physical world that began to take shape in the years between Descartes' birth and Newton's death, that persisted through the eighteenth century, and with immense enrichments and extensions still was the basic picture at the beginning of our own.

The second sketch has to do with the methods, the hopes, the program, and the style which seventeenth- and eighteenth-century science induced in men of learning and in men of affairs, with some of the special traits of that period of enlightenment which we recognize today as so deep in our tradition, as both so necessary to us and so inadequate.

More than one great revolution had ended and had been almost forgotten as the seventeenth century drew its picture of the physical world. A centuries-long struggle to decide whether it were rest or uniform motion that was the normal state of an undisturbed body no longer troubled men's minds: the great clarity, so foreign to everyday experience, that motion, as long as it was uniform, needed no cause and no explaining was Newton's first law. The less deep but far more turbulent Copernican revolution was history: the earth revolved about the sun. The physical world was matter in motion: the motion was to be understood in terms of the impetus or momentum of the bodies which would change only for cause, and of the force that was acting upon it to cause that change. This force was immediate and proximate. It produced a tendency for the impetus to change, and every course could be analyzed in terms of the forces deviating bodies from their uniform motions. The physical world was a world of differential law, a world connecting forces and motions at one point and at one instant with those at an infinitely near point in space and point of time; so that the whole course of the physical world could be broken down into finer and finer instants, and in each the cause of change assigned by a knowledge of forces.

Of these forces themselves the greatest in cosmic affairs —that which governed the planets in the heavens and the fall of projectiles on earth—had been found by Newton in the general law of gravity. Was this, too, something that spread from place to place, that was affected only instant by instant, point by point; or was it a property given as a whole, an interaction somehow ordained to exist between bodies remote from one another? Newton was never to answer this question; but he, and even more than he, Huygens, studying the propagation of light, were laying the foundations for a definite view—a view in which the void of the atomists would lose much of its emptiness and take on properties from the bodies which inhabited it, which in turn would affect bodies far away.

It was not until the nineteenth century and Faraday that the full richness of space began to be understood: how it could be the seat not only of gravitational forces produced by the mass of material particles but of electric and magnetic forces produced by their charges. Even in Newton's day it was clear that there were very strong forces at work in lending to material objects their solidity. Newton wrote:

> It seems probable to me, that God in the Beginning form'd Matter in solid, massy, hard, impenetrable, moveable Particles, of such Sizes and Figures, and with such other Properties and in such Proportion to Space, as most conduced to the End for which he formed them; and that these primitive Particles being Solids, are incomparably harder than any porous Bodies compounded of them; even so very hard, as never to wear or break in pieces; no ordinary Power being able to divide what God himself made one in the first Creation.

Newton saw that what held atoms together and made matter must be forces of inordinate strength, and he never considered their existence without a sense of mystery and awe. He did not know, nor do we today know, in what subtle way these forces might or might not be related to the forces of gravity.

But for many of his contemporaries and successors these questions appeared less pressing than the confidence that, once given the forces, the course of nature could be foretold and that, where the laws of gravity could be found, other forces would yield to observation and analysis. It is only in this century that we have begun to come to grips with other instances of antinomy, the apparent irreconcilability between the differential description of nature, point by point, instant to instant, and the total unique law and event. It is only in this century that we have had to recognize how unexpected and unfamiliar that relation between bodies and the atoms on the one hand, and that space full of light and electricity and gravitational forces on the other, could prove to be.

For the eighteenth century the world was a giant mechanism. It was a causal world, whether or not gravity and the other forces acting on bodies inhered in them by their nature or by God's will or that they, too, grew, through laws as rigorous as the laws of motion, from the properties induced in space by the bodies in it. All that happened had its full, complete, immediate, efficient cause. The great machine had a determinate course. A knowledge of its present and therefore its future for all time was, in principle, man's to obtain, and perhaps in practice as well. These objects with which the world was filled—the heavenly bodies, the impenetrable atoms and all things composed of them—were found by observation and by experiment; but it would have occurred to no one that their existence and their properties could be qualified or affected by the observations that told of them. The giant machine was not only causal and determinate; it was objective in the sense that no human act or intervention qualified its behavior.

A physical world so pictured could not but sharpen the great gulf between the object and the idea. It would do much to bring about that long, critical, and, in its later phase, irrational and mystical, view of the relations between the knower and the known that started with Locke and is perhaps even today not fully or happily ended.

It is, of course, clear that many developments in science that were to flower in the eighteenth and nineteenth centuries would soon moderate and complicate the harsh basic picture of the giant machine and of the vast gulf between it and the knowing human mind that thought about it and analyzed its properties. This is true of the great development of statistics, which in the end made room for human ignorance as an explicit factor in estimating the behavior of physical forces. It is true of chemistry, whose phenomena, whatever their ultimate description, looked so very little like the result of matter in motion. It is even more true of the biological sciences, where matter in motion, ever evident and inevitable, appears both at first sight and upon deeper analysis only marginally relevant to what makes biological forms interesting.

But with all of this, and with varying degrees of agreement and reservation, there was the belief that in the end all nature would be reduced to physics, to the giant machine. Despite all the richness of what men have learned about the world of nature, of matter and of space, of change and of life, we carry with us today an image of the giant machine as a sign of what the objective world is really like.

This view of the Newtonian world is oversimplified; perhaps any view of what men made of their new sciences, their new powers, and their new hopes will be simplified to the point of distortion. Science for the eighteenth century was not a finished undertaking; and, if men were overwhelmed with what they had learned, they were easily reminded of how much was still missing. A rational understanding of the world was not an understanding for one generation or one man, as it is alleged that it at one time appeared to be to Descartes. The immense discoveries of the recent past made it impossible to hold the view that all that was really worth knowing had long been known—a view that is a sort of parody, in any case, of the Renaissance.

This was a long journey on which men were embarked, the journey of discovery; they would need their wits and their resources and their forbearance if they were to get on with it. But it was a job in which progress was inevitable, and in which the style and success of physical science would tend to set the style for all undertakings of man's reason. What there is of direct borrowing from Newtonian physics for chemistry, psychology, or politics is mostly crude and sterile. What there is in eighteenth-century political and economic theory that derives from Newtonian methodology is hard for even an earnest reader to find. The absence of experiment and the inapplicability of Newtonian methods of mathematical analysis make that inevitable. These were not what physical science meant to the enlightenment.

It meant a style of thought, a habit of success, and an understanding of community quite typical for the age. These are to be found best in the learned communities that grew up in Europe and later in America—in the Royal Society and in the far more ambitious, far more revolutionary, far more programmatic French Academy. These communities were infused by a confidence in the power of reason and by a sense of improvement constant and almost inevitable in the condition of man's knowledge, and therefore of his actions and his life. They rest on a consensus of men, often seeing with their own eyes the crucial experiment that was to test or to confirm a theory; on the common experience of criticism and analysis; on the widespread use of mathematical methods with all the assurance of objectivity and precision that they give us. These were communities banded together for the promotion of knowledge—critical, rapacious to correct error, yet tolerant from knowing that error is an inevitable step in acquiring new knowledge. These were communities proud of their broad, non-sectarian, international membership, proud of their style and their wit, and with a wonderful sense of new freedom. One may recapture some sense of these communities from the writings of the time. The first history of the Royal Society is not truly a history but an apology, written when the society was only a few years old, explaining it, defending it against its critics. Bishop Sprat has this to say:

Their Purpose is, in short, to make faithful *Records* of all the Works of *Nature,* or *Art,* which can come within their Reach; that so the present Age, and Posterity, may be able to put a Mark on the Errors, which have been strengthened by long Prescription; to restore the Truths, that have lain neglected; to push on those, which are already known, to more various Uses; and to make the way more passable, to what remains unreveal'd. This is the Compass of their Design . . .

They have tried to put it into a Condition of perpetual Increasing, by settling an inviolable Correspondence between the Hand and the Brain. They have studied, to make it not only an Enterprise of one Season, or of some lucky Opportunity; but a Business of Time; a steady, a lasting, a popular, an uninterrupted Work . . .

It is to be noted, that they have freely admitted Men of different Religions, Countries, and Professions of Life. This they were oblig'd to do, or else they would come far short of the Largeness of their own Declarations. For they openly profess, not to lay the Foundation of an *English, Scotch, Irish, Popish,* or *Protestant* Philosophy; but a Philosophy of *Mankind.*

Reading this today, we can hardly escape a haunting sense of its timeliness and a certain nostalgia at how little the texture of our life conforms to these agreeable and noble ideals. We cannot perhaps wholly forget how much these communities owed to the long centuries of Christian life and Christian tradition; how much that they then took for granted in their inquiries and thoughts, in their whole style, derived from a way of life and a history which they were about to change beyond all recognition; and how deeply this, their program, could alter the very men and the very minds to whom their program would in time become entrusted.

These, however, were not reflections to darken much the eighteenth century or to cast real shadows on that great path of light, that renewed hope of men for a growing and growingly rational comprehension of their world and of themselves. At the very end of the century in another land largely nourished and fathered by the enlightenment, a gentleman and patriot wrote a letter. He wrote in answer to a young friend inquiring about his present course of study. He wrote in the last days of the Directorate, when the course of history was diverging in alarming and immense ways from that charted by the men of the French Academy. He wrote it about two years before he was to assume the Presidency of the United States, there for over a century to raise more firmly than ever before the standard of man's freedom, his progress, and his rational nature.

I am among those who think well of the human character generally. I consider man as formed for society, and endowed by nature with those dispositions which fit him for society. I believe also, with Condorcet, as mentioned in your letter, that his mind is perfectible to a degree of which we cannot as yet form any conception . . . science can never be retrograde; what is once acquired of real knowledge can never be lost. To preserve the freedom of the human mind then and freedom of the press, every spirit should be ready to devote himself to martyrdom; for as long as we may think as we will, and speak as we think, the condition of man will proceed in improvement. The generation which is going off the stage has deserved well of mankind for the struggles it has made, and for having arrested that course of despotism which had overwhelmed the world for thousands and thousands of years. If there seems to be danger that the ground they have gained will be lost again, that danger comes from the generation your contemporary. But that the enthusiasm which characterises youth should lift its parracide hands against freedom and science would be such a monstrous phaenomenon as I cannot place among possible things in this age and country.

The writer of the letter was Thomas Jefferson.

2.

SCIENCE AS ACTION:
RUTHERFORD'S WORLD

IT IS inherent in the very notion of culture and of tradition that there is a cumulative aspect to human life. The past underlies the present, qualifies and moderates it, in some ways limits it and in some ways enriches it. We understand Shakespeare better for having read Chaucer, and Milton for having read Shakespeare. We appreciate Trevelyan more for knowing Thucydides. We see Cézanne with better eyes for having looked also at Vermeer, and understand much more in Locke for knowing Aristotle, St. Matthew for knowing Job. But in actual fact we rather seldom bring a knowledge of the earlier to our first acquaintance with the later; and if it is true that Job throws light on Matthew, it is also true that Matthew throws light on Job. We can understand a great deal of what is written today, knowing little explicitly of what has been written in the past. We can and do know a great deal of what Shakespeare means and intends without any knowledge of those earlier men who altered and educated his sensibility.

The cumulative character of science is very different and very much more essential. It is one of the reasons for the great difficulty of understanding any science in which one has not largely become an expert—the science of which Hobbes wrote: "Of that nature, as none can understand it to be, but such as in good measure have attayned it."

There are at least two reasons for this: one has to do with the relation of later discoveries in science to earlier, and the other with the use that is made of earlier work in science as an instrument of progress. When we find out something new about the natural world this does not supersede what we knew before; it transcends it, and the transcendence takes place because we are in a new domain of experience, often made accessible only by the full use of prior knowledge. The work of Huygens and Fresnel on the wave properties of light is as necessary today as it ever was, although we know that there are properties of light which are left out in their account and their experience, properties which, in the context of atomic happenings, are decisive. Newton's law of gravitation and his equations of motion apply to and underlie immense realms of physical experience and are not made wrong by the fact that in other and still vaster spheres they must be replaced by the broader laws of Einstein. The chemical theory of valency has been explained, elucidated, and, to some small degree, extended by an understanding, in terms of the behavior of electrons and nuclei, of what goes on in chemical bonding; but the chemical theory of valency is not superseded and will presumably be used as long as man's interest in chemistry continues. The foundations of solid fact and the laws which describe it persevere through the whole course of science, to be refined and adapted to new contexts but never to be ignored or cast out.

But this is only a part of the story. It is a recurring experience of scientific progress that what was yesterday an object of study, of interest in its own right, becomes today something to be taken for granted, something understood and reliable, something known and familiar—a tool for further research and discovery. Sometimes the new instrument which is used to extend experience is a natural phenomenon, only barely qualified or controlled by the experimenter. We are familiar with the use of calcite crystals to produce two separate beams of polarized light. We know that the cosmic rays are both an object of investigation in themselves and a tool of hitherto unparalleled power for probing the properties and transmutations of primordial matter here on earth and in the laboratory. Sometimes past knowledge is embodied not in a natural phenomenon but in an invention, or in elaborate pyramids of invention, a new technology.

There are many well known and major examples of technological development during the last war which have added to the instruments of the investigator of the physical and biological world. We may recall two. Microwave radar—the generation, control, and detection of electromagnetic waves of relatively very short length—played a heroic part in the Battle of Britain. In the years since, it has provided powerful new means of investigating atomic, molecular, and even nuclear problems from which in actual fact subtle discoveries have been made about the laws of interaction of electrons and protons and neutrons.

The nuclear reactor embodies in its technology very recently acquired understanding of the fission processes in uranium and of the behavior of neutrons in their collisions with atomic nuclei; it is now an important tool whose controlled and well-understood radiations are telling us about properties of matter hitherto barely accessible. Artificially radioactive substances made in great profusion by atomic reactors enable us to follow the course of individual atoms in chemical and biological changes. In biology especially they may be an addition to our instrumental facilities and techniques comparable in importance with the microscope itself.

It is an oversimplification to say that technologies based upon recently discovered natural phenomena are taken as wholly for granted and as wholly known, but this is essentially the truth. They are added to the experimenter as a good tool is added to the artisan; as the pencil in the writer's hand ceases to be an object in itself and becomes almost a part of the writer; or as a horse under a good horseman becomes for the time being not an animal to be cared for and thought about but a part of the entity "horseman." Thus what has been learned and invented in science becomes an addition to the scientist, a new mode of perception, a new mode of his action.

There are some cautions to be added to this. No experimenter takes his equipment quite so much for granted that he fails to check whether in fact it is performing as it is supposed to perform; but the notion of how it is supposed to perform is for him in general a fixed thing not calling for further inquiry. This may be true even when the invention is a sample of practical art rather than a sample of true understanding. The photographic plate has served as an instrument of science for decades, during which its behavior was only very incompletely understood. Any machine can get out of order, and in a laboratory most machines do. The horse is shod and bridled and fed before he can become part of the horseman. Nevertheless we use what we have learned to go further. A perpetual doubting and a perpetual questioning of the truth of what we have learned is not the temper of science. If Einstein was led to ask not "What is a clock?" but "How, over great distances and with great precision, do we synchronize clocks?" that is not an illustration of the scepticism of science; it exemplifies rather the critical reason creating a new synthesis from paradoxes, anomalies, and bewilderments, which experiments carried on with new precision and in a new context brought into being.

All this means that science is cumulative in a quite special sense. We cannot really know what a contemporary experiment means unless we understand what the instruments and the knowledge are that are involved in its design. This is one reason why the growing edge of science seems so inaccessible to common experience. Its findings are defined in terms of objects and laws and ideas which were the science of its predecessors. This is why the student spends many long years learning the facts and arts which, in the acts of science, he will use and take for granted—why this long tunnel, at the end of which is the light of discovery, is so discouraging for the layman to enter, be he an artist, scholar, or man of affairs.

This conversion of an object of study into an instrument has its classic exemplification in Rutherford and the α-particle. This is a trail we will follow for some time. It will lead us to the heart of atomic physics. The α-particle, emitted by many naturally radioactive substances, identical with the nucleus of helium, was indeed a strong right arm for Rutherford and all his school in probing the atomic world. Rutherford's early works had been largely devoted to writing the wonderful natural history of the radioactive families—those which start with spontaneous changes in the heavy elements uranium and thorium. Part of the natural history was to discover the genetic relations between the various radioactive substances, some of them growing as a result of the decay of others and in turn giving rise to daughter products by further transmutation.

The natural history involves a chemical identification of the radioactive substances, the determination of the rapidity of their decay and of the alternative modes of decay, which some of them exhibit. It involves the recognition of three fundamentally different kinds of radiation, all of which appear at one stage or another in these family histories. This identification, which we shall meet again in later contexts, means learning some of the basic properties of the particles emitted. This identification, as we shall shortly see, is made possible by the fact that even a single such particle has readily detectable effects.

These properties include the mass of the particle and its electric charge. These have usually been found in the first instance by studying their behavior in large-scale electric and magnetic fields and applying Newton's laws to analyze their motion. These same methods give one a measure of the velocity or energy with which the particles are emitted, and of the loss of this energy as the particles pass through matter. Sometimes, at a later stage, the products of an atomic or nuclear disintegration can be more thoroughly studied. They may have more subtle electromagnetic properties than charge, such as a small magnetic moment. They may have structure or size. But the basic identifications can all be made in terms of the response of the radiations to familiar, large-scale, experimentally controllable situations like the classical electric and magnetic fields of our laboratory courses.

The α-particle of the naturally radioactive substances became for the middle years of Rutherford's life the sharpest experimental tool; it was to be supplemented and to some extent superseded only when artificially accelerated nuclei became available during the nineteen-thirties. The essential features of the experiments that have told us most about atoms and nuclei and the ingredients of matter are two: one has to do with structure, and the other with scale.

The structure of the experiment involves three parts: a probe, which is an object meant to explore or disturb matter in its natural state, typically with some degree of violence. This was the role of the α-particle. The second element is the target, which is some form of matter, whether pure or of controllable and manageable complications; and the third is the detector, which identifies and describes the objects emerging from the disturbance, whether they be the altered or the unaltered probe, or something knocked out of the target, or created in the collision, or something appearing long after the collision as evidence of a rearrangement of the collision products consequent upon the disturbance. This is not a universal pattern—this probe-target-detector assembly. The collision is not the only way of learning about atomic systems; but almost all of what we have learned has derived at least in part from such experiments and can be elucidated in terms of them.

As to scale, it is the scale that determines the possibility of detection. The events that are so studied—the collisions, transmutations—can typically be studied event by event, atom by atom. The reason for this lies in two circumstances: one is that in nuclear transformations, and even more so in transformations induced by cosmic rays and superaccelerators, the energy characteristic of a single atomic process is enormous compared to the chemical energies, and is sufficient to produce recognizable physical and chemical changes in hundreds of thousands or even millions of atoms.

The second circumstance lies in the art that has been devoted toward exploiting these energies in systems of detection. The detectors for Rutherford's experiments are by now familiar. One is the scintillation screen, where an a-particle creates a flash of light easily visible through a microscope at the point where it hits the screen. Another is the beautiful cloud chamber of C. T. R. Wilson, which is, according to legend, an outcome of the inventor's interest in the mist and clouds and rain of his native Scotland. In this cloud chamber the track of a charged particle is marked by the occurrence of innumerable small yet readily visible droplets of water or other liquid close to where the particles passed. A third is the counter, in which the electrical disturbance produced in a gas by the passage of a charged particle gives rise to a substantial electrical discharge, which can be amplified and analyzed by electronic circuitry.

These detectors have been supplemented by many, many others; and the precision and power of electronic amplification and analysis have been developed into a great art. The detector of atomic physics still characteristically is designed to take advantage of the very great energy involved in the changes of a single atom, and of the power to amplify this energy almost at will to make it accessible. The clicking counters and flashing lights and occasionally even the ringing bells of a modern nuclear laboratory make the doings of individual atoms very vivid and immediate, and make the subtle atoms of Epicurus or of Newton seem very private and remote.

Rutherford and his probing α-particles and detectors are old history, dating back roughly some forty years. They are basic alike to atomic and nuclear physics, basic as a foundation for the great revolution in science which it is my principal purpose to describe, and for the further developments at the very forefront of contemporary discovery that have us today perplexed and bemused. With his α-particles, obtained from natural radioactivity, Rutherford discovered the atomic nucleus and the nuclear model of the atom; with some help from other evidence he discovered the mass and the charge of the various atomic nuclei and thus rationalized Mendelyeev's table of the elements. With the α-particles, he was able to touch nuclear matter itself and measure its dimensions. He showed that it could be transmuted; he identified at least some of its ingredients.

For the most part, α-particles when they pass through a bit of matter are not very much deflected or changed in direction; they are gradually slowed down; but occasionally a particle will change its direction of motion very greatly. It will be scattered through a large angle; it will act as though some great force had disturbed it, as though it had hit something quite small and quite hard. The law describing these deflections is Rutherford's law; and to it he gave a simple meaning: there are forces acting on the α-particles; they are not unfamiliar to physics. They are the electric repulsion between the charge of the atomic nucleus and the charge of the α-particle—the same force which manifests itself when two positively charged pith balls push each other apart in an elementary demonstration. The balls repel each other because the two charges are similar; and the repulsion is described by Coulomb's law —very much the same law as Newton's law of gravitation. The repulsion is inversely proportional to the square of the separation of the charges. The charge of the atomic nucleus is a multiple of that of the proton—the nucleus of hydrogen. The multiple is the atomic number, which determines the number of electrons in the atom, and almost all the chemical properties of the element, and the position in the periodic table of that element. The mass of the nucleus is almost the whole mass of the atom as expressed by its atomic weight. This charge and mass is concentrated in a small volume. Everywhere outside it, the α-particle feels only the electric field.

By using α-particles fast enough to overcome the electric repulsion, and using light elements for which the charge and therefore the repulsion are not too great, Rutherford found that occasionally α-particles penetrated to a different domain entirely, where very strong forces, not electric forces, deflected them. In this way he found the dimensions of the nucleus itself: roughly one part in 10,-000 of the dimensions of the atom as a whole. This characterized the nucleus as a region of incredibly high density, of many millions of tons per cubic inch. Rutherford discovered even more: he was able to show that when fast a-particles penetrated nuclear matter things other than a-particles emerged from the *mêlée*. In experiments undertaken during the First World War, and justified by Rutherford as of greater importance than any contribution he could then make to the prosecution of that war, Rutherford for the first time induced by human action the transmutation of an atomic nucleus, knocking out of the nucleus of nitrogen a nucleus of hydrogen, or proton, and starting a chain of events which led, among many things, to man's release of atomic energy, to what may some day be judged the most compelling argument of all for putting an end to war itself.

The story went on from there. Before we revert to the nuclear model of the atom and how oddly different its properties are from any we can understand on the basis of Newtonian physics, we may follow sketchily and partially this course of discovery with probe, target, and detector that Rutherford initiated and that has continued until the present day. Twenty years ago, using the same a-particles as probes, Chadwick managed to identify another survivor of the disturbance, another ingredient of the nucleus, the neutron, which has roughly the proton's mass but no charge, and thus to lay the foundations for an elementary view of nuclear composition. The nucleus is made up of neutrons and protons—enough protons to account for its charge, the atomic number; enough neutrons to account

for the excess of its atomic weight over its atomic number
—held together in their tiny volume by strong forces
wholly dissimilar from those of electricity and magnetism,
whose description even today is a far from completely
solved problem.

Chadwick's neutrons, in their turn, became probes, inducing nuclear transmutations very copiously, because
they were not kept away from nuclei by the positive nuclear charge. Their use led, in the years just before the
war, to Hahn's discovery that, when uranium was transmuted by being hit by neutrons, among the products was
barium, a large half of the original nucleus, but only
about half—and thus to nuclear fission.

Even this was only the beginning. In the very energetic
particles of cosmic radiation, in the nuclei accelerated by
giant modern accelerators to energies a hundredfold those
of Rutherford's α-particles, we have found new probes to
elicit new phenomena; the story of sub-nuclear matter began to unfold and ramify. A whole new family of hitherto
unknown, and, for the most part, unrecognized and unexpected objects began to emerge from the nuclear encoun-
ters. The first of these were the various mesons, some
charged and some uncharged, about ten times lighter than
the proton and some hundreds of times heavier than the
electron. In the last years there have appeared in increasing variety objects heavier than the mesons, other objects
heavier even than protons, whose names are still being
changed, from month to month, by solemn conferences.
Physicists call them vaguely, and rather helplessly, "the

new particles." They are without exception unstable, as in the neutron. They disintegrate after a time which varies from one millionth to less than a billionth of a second into other lighter components. Some of these components are in turn unfamiliar to physics and are themselves in turn unstable. We do not know how to give a clear meaning to this question. We do not know why they have the mass and charge that they do; why they and just they exist; why they disintegrate as they do; why in most cases they last as long as they do, or anything much about them. They are the greatest puzzle in today's physics.

But all this is now; and these were not the puzzles of Rutherford's day. To these we shall turn in the next lectures. They become manifest when we try to deduce and describe the properties of Rutherford's atom in terms of Newtonian mechanics. This attempted description failed. The atoms of nature are radically, dramatically, unlike atoms, composed as Rutherford found of electrons and small nuclei, subject to the forces Rutherford discovered and described, and moving according to Newton's laws. The failure of this classical description turned out to be a major clue, one of the few major clues, in the atomic story. We learned, before the story was finished, that more than Newtonian mechanics would have to be modified if we were to understand and describe our experience with atomic systems. We would have to alter our ideas on very fundamental points, on causality, for instance, and even on the nature of the objectivity of parts of the physical world. We were to be reminded, in a quite unexpected way, of the nature and limitations, as well as the power, of human knowledge itself. It is largely for this reason that the story of atomic discovery has appeared to me so full of instruction for us all, for layman as well as specialist. For it has recalled to us traits of old wisdom that we can well take to heart in human affairs.

Before these great changes could be completed, and the strange situation elucidated, many new ideas and methods of description were to be introduced. We learned words new for us, like "quantum," and "state," words like "correspondence" and "complementarity," words with a new meaning for physics. Of these the word "correspondence" came to stand for the conservative and traditional traits of the new physics, that bound it to the physics of the past; whereas "complementarity" described, as we shall come to see, those new features, unknown to the physics of Newton, that have broadened and humanized our whole understanding of the natural world.

Time and experience have clarified, refined, and enriched our understanding of these notions. Physics has changed since then. It will change even more. But what we have learned so far, we have learned well. If it is radical and unfamiliar and a lesson that we are not likely to forget, we think that the future will be only more radical and not less, only more strange and not more familiar, and that it will have its own new insights for the inquiring human spirit.

3.

A SCIENCE IN CHANGE

OUR understanding of atomic physics, of what we call the quantum theory of atomic systems, had its origins at the turn of the century and its great synthesis and resolutions in the nineteen-twenties. It was a heroic time. It was not the doing of any one man; it involved the collaboration of scores of scientists from many different lands, though from first to last the deeply creative and subtle and critical spirit of Niels Bohr guided, restrained, deepened, and finally transmuted the enterprise. It was a period of patient work in the laboratory, of crucial experiments and daring action, of many false starts and many untenable conjectures. It was a time of earnest correspondence and hurried conferences, of debate, criticism, and brilliant mathematical improvisation.

For those who participated, it was a time of creation; there was terror as well as exaltation in their new insight. It will probably not be recorded very completely as history. As history, its re-creation would call for an art as high as the story of Oedipus or the story of Cromwell, yet in a realm of action so remote from our common experience that it is unlikely to be known to any poet or any historian. In other ways, there will be such times again. Most of us are convinced that today, in our present probings in the sub-atomic and sub-nuclear world, we are laying the groundwork for another such time for us and for our sons. The great growth of physics, the vast and increasingly complicated laboratories of the mid-twentieth century, the increasing sophistication of mathematical analysis, have altered many of the conditions of this new period of crisis. We do not think that they will have altered its heroic and creative character.

When quantum theory was first taught in the universities and institutes, it was taught by those who had participated, or had been engaged spectators, in its discovery. Some of the excitement and wonder of the discoverer was in their teaching; now, after two or three decades, it is taught not by the creators but by those who have learned from others who have learned from those creators. It is taught not as history, not as a great adventure in human understanding, but as a piece of knowledge, as a set of techniques, as a scientific discipline to be used by the student in understanding and exploring new phenomena in the vast work of the advance of science, or its application to invention and to practical ends. It has become not a subject of curiosity and an object of study but an instrument of the scientist to be taken for granted by him, to be used by him, to be taught to him as a mode of action, as we teach our children to spell and to add.

What we must attempt to do in these talks is wholly different. This is no school to learn the arts of atomic physics. Even those prior arts—the experimental tools, the mathematical powers, the theories, inventions, instruments, and techniques which defined the problems of atomic physics, which established the paradoxes, described the phenomena, and underlay the need for synthesis—are not known to us of our own experience. We must talk of our subject not as a community of specialized scientists but as men concerned with understanding, through analogy, description, and an act of confidence and trust, what other people have done and thought and found. So men listen to accounts of soldiers returning from a campaign of unparalleled hardship and heroism, or of explorers from the high Himalayas, or of tales of deep illness, or of a mystic's communion with his God. Such stories tell little of what the teller has to tell. They are the threads which bind us in community and make us more than separate men.

Here, then, we have our atoms. Their ingredients have been made manifest by Rutherford and his α-particles, as have the forces that act between the ingredients, and by probing with electrons and with light as well as with α-particles. There is the nucleus, with almost the whole of the atom's mass and almost none of its size, and with a charge which is measured by the atomic number, equal to the number of electrons that surround the nucleus in the normal atom. We have the simple laws of attraction and repulsion, familiar from the large-scale, everyday experience with electricity. Unlike charges attract and like repel; and the forces, like Newton's, decrease inversely with the square of their separation.

In Rutherford's day it seemed reasonable, as it no longer entirely does today in facing our modern physics, to subdivide the problem of atomic structure into three questions: what are the ingredients of the atom; what are the forces, and the laws of force, acting between these ingredients; how in response to those forces do the ingredients move? We know that even in atomic problems this division is not completely rigorous; but the refinements are minor and have largely proved tractable. They consist of taking into account the effect of the motion of the particles themselves on the forces between them and, in some cases, the distortion of the properties of particles, very small itself in the atomic structures, by the presence of other particles and the forces that they exert. It is surely not wholly true of the nucleus that these distortions are small; and in the strange objects which emerge so readily when nuclei undergo violent collisions we have persuasive, if indirect, evidence for that.

The atom, then, has a massive charged nucleus; the atom as a whole is neutral and 10,000 to 100,000 times as far across as its tiny nuclear core. The rest of the atom is composed of electrons and electric fields—electrons that are the universal ingredients of matter, the determinants of almost all its chemical properties and of most of its familiar physical properties as well. There will be as many electrons in the atom as the atomic number, the nuclear charge; this makes the atom as a whole neutral. There will be one electron in hydrogen and thirteen in aluminum and ninety-two in uranium. These are the ingredients; and the laws of force, complex only in the last refinements, are basically simple. The electron feels an attractive Coulomb force exerted by the nucleus, attractive since the electron and nucleus are oppositely charged, and once again falling off with distance in the same way as gravitational forces according to Newton's law. For hydrogen, this means a simple situation: two bodies with a force between them identical in structure with that which the sun exerts on the planets; two bodies small enough compared to the atom's size so that they almost never touch, and the properties of their contact can have little influence. The law of forces has been verified not only by probing with particles, by which it was originally discovered, but by probing with electrons themselves, in the first instances by the beta rays of naturally radioactive substances. For other atoms there is in addition the electrical repulsion between the several electrons, balancing to some extent the nuclear attraction. And there is, further, the well-known mathematical complication of describing quantitatively the behavior of a system with many particles.

But with hydrogen this should not be so. Here we have essentially a single light body moving in a simple and well-known force. The description of this system should be a perfect example of Newtonian dynamics, and should, in its refinements, be intelligible in terms of all that the nineteenth century had discovered about the behavior of charged particles in motion and the electromagnetic radiation produced when they are accelerated.

But it did not turn out that way. To what appeared to be the simplest questions, we will tend to give either no answer or an answer which will at first sight be reminiscent more of a strange catechism than of the straightforward affirmatives of physical science. If we ask, for instance, whether the position of the electron remains the same, we must say "no"; if we ask whether the electron's position changes with time, we must say "no"; if we ask whether the electron is at rest, we must say "no"; if we ask whether it is in motion, we must say "no." The Buddha has given such answers when interrogated as to the conditions of a man's self after his death; but they are not familiar answers for the tradition of seventeenth- and eighteenth-century science.

Let us review, then, what a hydrogen atom should be like if we could apply Newton's laws and the whole classical picture of matter in motion to the simple model. The electron is held to its nucleus as the earth is to the sun, or as is Venus. It should revolve in an ellipse, as Kepler found and Newton explained. The size of the ellipse could be varied from atom to atom as the orbits of the planets are different, depending on how it was formed and what its history, and so should the shape of the orbits, whether they are narrow or round. There should be no fixed size for a hydrogen atom and no fixed properties; and when we disturb one by one of our probings, or when it is disturbed in nature, we would not expect it to return to a size and shape at all similar to that from which it started. This is not all—there are more recondite points. When a charge moves in anything but a straight line, it should send out electromagnetic radiation. This is what we see in every radio antenna. As far as our model goes, this radiation should in time sap the energy of the electron to make up for the energy that has been sent out in the form of light waves; and the ellipses on which the electron moves should get smaller and smaller as it gets nearer to its attractive sun and loses its energy. For a system about the size of the hydrogen atom as we know it in nature, a few hundredths of a millionth of an inch across, this process should go very rapidly; and the atom should become far, far smaller than atomic dimensions in very much less than a millionth of a second. The color of the light that the electron radiates should be determined by the period of its revolution; it too should be random, differing from orbit to orbit, differing from time to time as the orbits shrink and alter. This is the picture which classical physics—Newtonian physics—predicts for the hydrogen atom, if Rutherford's model is right.

It could hardly be further from the truth. By all we know, hydrogen atoms if undisturbed are all identical. They are the same size and each has the same properties as any other, whatever its history, provided only that it has had a chance to recover from any disturbance. They last indefinitely. We think of them, rightly, as completely stable and unchanging. When they are undisturbed, they do not radiate light or any other electromagnetic radiation, as indeed they could not if they are to remain unaltered. When they are disturbed, they sometimes do radiate, but the color of the light that they emit is not random and continuous but falls in the sharp lines of the hydrogen spectrum. The very stability, extent, and definiteness is not at all understandable on the basis of classical physics; and indeed on the basis of classical physics there is no length that we can define in terms of the masses and charges of the ingredients of the atom, and that is even roughly of the actual dimensions of the atom.

In other respects, too, the atomic system shows a peculiar lack of continuity wholly at variance with the properties of Newtonian dynamics. If we probe atoms with a stream of electrons, for instance, the electrons will typically lose some of their initial energy, but these losses are not random in amount. They correspond to definite, well-defined energy gaps, characteristic for the atom in question, reproducible and not too hard to measure. When an atom is irradiated by light, an electron will be ejected, if and only if the energy of that light exceeds a certain minimum known as the photo-electric threshold. Indeed, it was this discovery which led Einstein in the early years of the century to a finding about light almost equally revolutionary for our understanding of light and for our understanding of atomic systems. This finding, to be more precise, is that as one alters the frequency of the light that shines on a body, the energy of the electrons ejected increases linearly with the frequency; linearly—that means proportionally. The constant of proportionality, which connects energy with frequency, is the new symbol of the atomic domain. It is called Planck's constant, or the quantum of action, and it gives a measure of energy in terms of frequency. It is the heraldic symbol over the gateway to the new world; and it led Einstein to the bold, though at the time hardly comprehensible, conclusion that light, which we know as an electromagnetic disturbance of rapidly changing electrical fields, which we know as a continuous phenomenon propagating from point to point and from time to time like a wave, is also and is nevertheless corpuscular, consisting of packets of energy determined by the frequency of the light and by Planck's constant. When a material system absorbs light, it absorbs such a packet, or quantum, of energy, neither less nor more; and the discontinuous nature of the energy exchanges between an atom and an electron is paralleled by the discontinuous nature of the energy exchanged when radiation is absorbed or emitted.

We shall have to come back more than once to light as waves, and light as quanta; but how radical a problem of understanding this presents can be seen at once from all of classical optics, from the work of Huygens and its mathematical elaboration by Fresnel, and even more completely from its electromagnetic interpretation by Maxwell. We know that light waves interfere. We know, that is, that if there are two sources of light, the intensity of the light to be found at some other place will not necessarily be just composed of the sum of that which comes from the two sources; it may be more and it may be less. We know from unnumbered attempts how to calculate, and how to calculate correctly, what the interference of the sources will turn out to be. If we have light impinging on a screen which is opaque and there are two holes in the screen, not too large and not too far apart in the terms of the wave length, the wavelets that come from one of the holes will be added to those that come from the other. Where two crests of these wavelets coincide, we shall have more light than the sum of the two. Where a crest and a trough coincide, we shall have less; and so we observe and understand and predict and are quite confident of these phenomena of interference.

Try for a moment to describe this in the terms of the passage of particles of quanta. If one of those quanta which characterize both the emission of light at the source and its detection—let us say, by the eye or by the photographic plate or photo-cell on the far side of the screen—if a quantum passes through one of the holes, how can the presence of the other hole through which it did not pass affect its destiny? How can there be any science or any prediction if the state of affairs remote from the trajectory of the quantum can determine its behavior? Just this question and our slow answer to it will start us on the unravelling of the physics of the atomic world.

The first great step, taken long before the crisis of quantum theory, was to find a way of describing atomic behavior, not forgetting the mechanics and electrodynamics of the past, but knowing that one had here to do with something new and different, and necessarily postponing the question of the connection of that which is new with the old laws. This is Bohr's first theory. It has given us the symbol of the atomic world: the nucleus and a series of circles and ellipses represent in a pictorial way the states of the atom. We use it today, though we know in far more detail and far more completely what Bohr knew when he proposed it, that it could be at best a temporary and partial analogy. This was Bohr's first postulate: that in every atom there were stationary states whose stability and uniqueness could not be understood in terms of classical dynamics. The lowest one, the one with the least energy, the ground state, is truly stable. Unless we disturb it, it will last unaltered. The others are called excited states, and they may be excited by collision or radiation or other disturbance. They, too, are stable in a sense incomprehensible in terms of Newton's theory. Their stability is not absolute though. Just as these states could be reached by transition induced by collision or disturbance, so an atom may return to states of lower energy, whether by further collision or spontaneously. In these spontaneous changes it gives out that radiation which is the analog of the radiation which in classical theory would make all motion unstable. In simple cases, the energy of these stationary states and some of the properties such as their shape are identical with or similar to the energy of some of the properties of Newtonian orbits. But this stops being true when we go even from hydrogen to helium, with its two electrons. It is only partially true in hydrogen; and the rules which Bohr laid down for determining the character of the orbits that would correspond to stationary states, the so-called quantum conditions, were from the first recognized by him as incomplete and provisional. We know now that the states are in fact nothing like orbits at all; that the element of change with time, which is inherent in an orbit, is missing from these states; and that in fact the very notion of an orbit can be applied to the motion of matter only when the stationary state is not defined, and that a stationary state can exist only when there is no possibility of describing an orbit at all.

That was the first rule. And what is the second? The second rule is that an atom can change only by passing from state to state; that its energy changes by the difference in energy between the states; and that, when this exchange of energy occurs in the absorption, emission, or scattering of light, the frequency of the light will be related to the energy by the relation of Einstein and of Planck. The energy will be the frequency multiplied by the quantum of action; thus atomic spectra directly reveal energy differences between states, and by this the whole field of spectroscopy becomes evidence for the location and the properties of atomic states, and we begin to learn what properties of these states are like those of classical orbits and what are unlike.

But what are we to think of the transitions themselves? Do they take place suddenly? Are they very quick motions, executed in going from one orbit to another? Are they causally determined? Can we say, that is, when an atom will pass from one of its states to another as we disturb it; and can we find what it is that determines that time? To all these questions, the answer would turn out to be "no." What we learned to ask was what determined not the moment of the transition but the probability of the transition. What we needed to understand was not the state of affairs during the transition but the impossibility of visualizing the transition—an even more radical impossibility than with the states themselves—in terms of the motion of matter. We learned to accept, as we later learned to understand, that the behavior of an atomic system is not predictable in detail; that of a large number of atomic systems with the same history, in, let us say, the same state, statistical prediction was possible as to how they would act if they were let alone and how they would respond to intervention; but that nowhere in our battery of experimental probings would we find one to say what one individual atom would in fact do. We saw in the very heart of the physical world an end of that complete causality which had seemed so inherent a feature of Newtonian physics.

How could all this be and yet leave the largely familiar world intact as we knew it? Large bodies are, of course, made up of atoms. How could causality for bullets and machines and planets come out of acausal atomic behavior? How could trajectories, orbits, velocities, accelerations, and positions re-emerge from this strange talk of states, transitions, and probabilities? For what was true yesterday would be true still, and new knowledge could not make old knowledge false. Is there a possible unity between the two worlds and what is its nature?

This is the problem of correspondence. Whatever the laws which determine the behavior of light or of electrons in atoms or other parts of the atomic world, as we come closer and closer to the familiar ground of large-scale experience, these laws must conform more and more closely to those we know to be true. This is what we call the principle of correspondence. In its formulation the key is the quantum of action, whose finiteness characterizes the new features of atomic physics. And so the physicist says that, where actions are large compared to the quantum of action, the classical laws of Newton and Maxwell will hold. What this tends to mean in practice is that when mass and distances are big compared to those of the electron and the atom's size, classical theory will be right. Where energies are large and times long compared to atomic energies and times, we shall not need to correct Newton. Where this is so, the statistical laws of atomic physics will lead to probabilities more and more like certitudes, and the acausal features of atomic theory will be of no moment, and in fact lost in the lack of precision with which questions about large events will naturally be put.

In Bohr's hands and those of the members of his school, this correspondence principle was to prove a powerful tool. It did not say what the laws of atomic physics were, but it said something about them. They must in this sense be harmonious with, and ultimately reducible to, those of large-scale physics. And when to this principle was added the growing conviction that the laws of atomic physics must deal not with the Newtonian position, velocity, and acceleration that characterized a particle but with the observable features of atoms—the energies and properties of stationary states, the probabilities of transitions between these states—the groundwork was laid for the discovery of quantum mechanics.

The principle of correspondence—this requirement that the new laws of atomic mechanics should merge with those of Newtonian mechanics for large bodies and events—thus had great value as an instrument of discovery. Beyond that, it illustrates the essential elements of the relation of new discovery and old knowledge in science; the old knowledge, as the very means for coming upon the new, must in its old realm be left intact; only when we have left that realm can it be transcended.

A discovery in science, or a new theory, even when it appears most unitary and most all-embracing, deals with some immediate element of novelty or paradox within the framework of far vaster, unanalyzed, unarticulated reserves of knowledge, experience, faith, and presupposition. Our progress is narrow; it takes a vast world unchallenged and for granted.

This is one reason why, however great the novelty or scope of new discovery, we neither can, nor need, rebuild the house of the mind very rapidly. This is one reason why science, for all its revolutions, is conservative. This is why we will have to accept the fact that no one of us really will ever know very much. This is why we shall have to find comfort in the fact that, taken together, we know more and more.

4.

ATOM AND VOID IN THE THIRD MILLENNIUM

IN EXPLORING the atomic world, we have traveled to a new country, strange for those who have lived in the familiar world of Newtonian physics, strange even to Newton's own view of wonder and pre-vision. "God in the Beginning," he wrote, "form'd Matter in solid, massy, hard, impenetrable, movable Particles. . . ."

We have our atoms; we are trying to understand them. We have the simplest of the atoms, hydrogen, with a single proton for its nucleus and a single electron to make it up. But the ingredients do not follow Newton's laws of motion. Atoms of hydrogen appear to be all alike; they have a fixed size; they are stable and not transitory; the light that they emit is not what an electron circling in ever smaller ellipses would radiate. They have a stability that does not derive from Newtonian mechanics. When they are disturbed by light or electrons or other matter, they take up energy in definite quanta characteristic for the atom. They are described in terms of states—states that are not orbits, though they have some of the properties of some special orbits. The states are stable, or almost stable. Transition between them, occasioned by disturbance, or occurring spontaneously with the emission of light, occurs by chance. We do not know the cause of the individual transition but only, at best, their probable distribution in time; nor do we have, in terms of space and time and trajectory, any picture whatever of what these transitions may be. These acausal atoms compose the familiar world of large bodies, orbits, and Newton's laws. The laws that describe atomic behavior, the stationary states and transitions, reduce by correspondence, when applied to large systems, to Newton's laws.

The discovery of these laws by Heisenberg could itself have led to all we now know of quantum theory, but it was supplemented as a matter of history by new discoveries in related fields which make the task of understanding and exposition simpler and more direct. Yet even these are both unfamiliar and abstract; I fear that no exposition can be wholly without difficulty.

Our problem has to do with the so-called duality of wave and particle. On the one hand we have light, described in detail as a continuous electromagnetic wave with electric and magnetic fields, changing with a frequency that determines the light's color, and with an amplitude that determines its intensity. The waves of light differ from radio waves only in one respect: their wave length is much shorter. They differ obviously from the waves we see on water, which are the more or less regular displacement of matter. But when we talk here of waves, in this account of wave-particle duality, as we shall have to, it will mean something quite abstract, something common to light, radio, and water waves.

It will mean a state of affairs distributed in space and propagating with time, sometimes a harmonic like a pure note of sound and sometimes irregular like noise. It will mean that these disturbances in general add, so that two crests reinforce, and a crest and a trough tend to cancel. It will mean that the sum of two effects may not be greater than either, but smaller, as the phases of crest and trough indicate. It will mean that, if we leave more than one alternative for a particle or for light to go from one place to another, the chance of arriving may be greater than the sum of the chances or smaller than the sum of the chances, because of this interference of the waves that represent the alternatives.

When we deal with light, we deal with such waves; but we also deal, as Einstein discovered, with something sharp, discrete, and discontinuous—the light quantum. Whenever light acts on matter, or is produced by it, we find packets of defined energy and impulse, related to their frequency and their wave number by the universal proportionality of the quantum of action. How were these quanta to be thought of? Were they guided by the waves? Were they the waves? Were the waves an illusion, after all?

This turned out to be a universal quandary. De Broglie suggested and later Davison found that there were waves associated with electrons. Specifically Davison's experiment showed that electrons, too, when they are scattered by the regular disturbance of a natural crystal, exhibit the same signs of interference, the same unmistakable signature of the super-position of waves as light and as X-rays; and later experiments showed that this is true of all the other particles as well—protons, neutrons, and the atoms themselves. It would be true of large objects also were it not that their wave length is small, because of smallness of Planck's constant, and becomes completely insignificant compared with their dimensions and with any practical possibility of determining their location and outline.

All the questions which puzzled men about the relations of Einstein's quanta and Maxwell's waves were thus to be equally sharp and equally troublesome for the wave and particle properties of matter. The resolution of these questions is the heart of atomic theory. They were brought to the point of crisis by another great discovery—Schroedinger's discovery of his wave equation.

In its original, bold form this was the discovery of a simple law for the propagation of electron waves—a natural generalization of the connection between wave number and impulse, between energy and frequency, a generalization nevertheless adequate to describe the gross features of atomic systems and most of the familiar properties of matter. This equation had many sorts of solutions. Some were stationary, unchanging in time, with a frequency and energy that corresponded to the stationary states of atoms. This same equation had other solutions of a very different kind, representing the trajectory of an electron as it might be seen crossing the Wilson cloud chamber. It had still other solutions, compounded by addition of several stationary states with their several proper frequencies. These were not stationary but varied in time with frequencies corresponding to the spectrum of atoms and molecules.

But what were these waves? What did they describe? How were they related to the ways in which we observe and study atomic systems, to Rutherford's probings, to the collisions and disturbances of atoms? Schroedinger understood that in some sense the world of classical physics would emerge from his equation, whenever the wave lengths were small enough; then the trajectories for bodies and planets would be like the geometric paths of light, the rays of optics. But what would the waves mean when this was not the case?

It would have been no answer to this question to attempt to interpret the waves as an essentially mechanical disturbance in some underlying mechanical medium; for the questions which needed answering had to do with the problems of stationary states, and the behavior of electrons, and not with a sub-stratum inaccessible to observation. Nor was such a path followed. The discouraging outcome of an analogous attempt with electromagnetic waves was conclusive. It did not seem reasonable, nor in fact has it ever proved possible, at a time when the very foundations of classical mechanics were being altered, to reinterpret this revolution in classical mechanical terms.

There was another false start. It was at one time suggested that the waves, as they spread and moved, in some sense represented the changing shape, extension, and flow of the electron itself; when the disturbance grew larger the electron grew larger; when the wave moved faster the electron moved faster. But to this interpretation there was an insuperable obstacle. Whenever we looked for the position of the particle, looked not directly with the eye, but with the natural extension of looking with a microscope, we did not find it spread out; we never found part of it in the place where we were looking. Either it was there or it was not there—the whole or none of it. Whenever we tried to measure the velocity of an electron or its impulse, we never found that part of it was moving with one speed and part with another; there was always one electron, one velocity, one answer to an experimental inquiry. The spreading of the waves in space thus did not mean that the electron itself spread; it meant that the probability or likelihood of our finding the electron, when we look for it, spread as the wave does.

And thus it was that these waves were recognized as describing a state of affairs, as summarizing information we had about the electron, as very much more abstract waves indeed than we had hitherto encountered in physics. Their interpretation was statistical as well as abstract: where a disturbance was large, there we were likely to find the electron if we looked for it; where it was small, unlikely. If the disturbance had ripples in which a certain wave length was prominent, a measurement of the momentum would be likely to give us a value corresponding to that wave length. This clearly is qualitative talk. Quantitative rules for assigning a wave function to describe the outcome of an observation—or of other certain forms of knowledge, such as that of an atom in its state of lowest energy— needed to be, could be, and were developed; and they are a part of quantum theory. Their exposition presupposes some mathematical talk and calls at least for a blackboard. Similarly, the simple rules which relate the magnitude or properties of a wave function to the expectations that it implies for one or another observation are a rigorous and necessary part of the theory. But with these bonds to tie the wave to our knowledge and to interpret it for our prediction, the basis of the new physics has been laid.

It is a statistical physics, as indeed might have been expected from the statistical features of atomic transitions. Its predictions are in the form of assertions of probability and only rarely and specially in the form of certitudes. With this in mind, let us look again at our problem of interference, and of the two holes.

Let us think of an opaque screen with two holes in it. Let us think of light, if we will; or, better still, let us think of electrons of a given velocity and therefore a given wave length and direction. We can do two experiments with a source of electrons. In one, each hole in turn will be open for a little, while the other is closed; in the other, both holes will be open together. If we register the electrons on the far side of the screen, for instance, with a photographic plate, we see that the two patterns are radically different. In the one case, we have a transmission through each of the holes separately, with the characteristic diffraction pattern for that wave length and for holes of that diameter. These patterns are just added to one another on the photographic film. But if both holes are open at the same time, something else happens. The waves that come through one interfere with those that come through the other; spots that were blackened before are now untouched and new spots appear where the electrons do arrive.

If we try to think of this in terms of following the electrons through one or the other of the holes, we cannot understand how it can make any difference whether that hole through which the electron did not pass is open or shut; yet it does. If we argue that the effect can be traced to the interaction of electrons passing through the two holes, we can disprove this by noting that the pattern is not affected by reducing the number of electrons to the point where there almost never are two passing through the two holes at the same time. What we are observing is something characteristic of the behavior of single particles, not of the interaction of several.

We are thus led to say that in this experiment a knowledge of which hole the electron passed through is in principle inaccessible to us, that it is just the possibility of its

passing through one or the other that leads to the characteristic new interference phenomena, the new light spots
and the new dark spots on the photographic film. We conclude that, if we should make provision for registering
through which hole the electron went, such as looking for
it or observing the small push that it gives to the screen as
it passes through, we would destroy the interference effects. We would then have the same result as if we had in
fact opened and shut the holes successively.

We see the connection between these conclusions and the
description of the state of affairs by a wave field in qualitative terms, rather closely paralleling the arguments that
were made quantitative in the uncertainty principle of
Heisenberg.

For we note that, if we were sure that the electron passed
through one of the holes, the wave field would have to be
restricted to that region; and that, if this were true, it
would have to be composed not of a single wave length, or
approximately a single one, but of waves of enough different wave lengths so that they can reinforce each other at
one hole and vanish at the other; and we know that such
waves have lost the coherent quality necessary for interference. A little more generally, the waves of a single wave
length will correspond to an electron of a definite velocity
or impulse, but in an ill-defined or undefined position; the
waves that are localized to represent a definition of position will be broadly scattered in wave length and represent
an undefined velocity or impulse. This complementary re-
striction on the degree to which a wave field can represent

both a well-defined position and a well-defined impulse is universal; it is measured by the quantum of action. It holds not only for electrons but for the more complicated waves that describe complex systems, for atoms and nuclei and more composite bits of matter and more elementary ones. And the very fact that no wave field can give that complete definition of the position and velocity of an object which was taken for granted in classical physics is also a description of the limitation on the observations which in the real world we shall manage to make. It represents the fact that, when we study a system, making an experiment or an observation on it, we may—and in general we will, if we have prior knowledge before the experiment—be losing in whole or in part that prior knowledge. The experiment itself—that is, the physical interactions between the system and the equipment that we are using to study it—will not only alter what we previously knew, but will in general alter it in a way which cannot be followed without invalidating the measurement or observation we have undertaken.

To cite but one example: if in the problem of the two holes we try to detect which hole the electron has passed through by noticing the push that it gives to the screen at that point, we shall have to leave a part of the screen free to respond to the push; and by this we lose all certitude as to where that part of the screen was when that electron passed through it. Many complex and detailed studies have been made of how this limitation of knowledge occurs in an experiment; but since the principle of complementarity, and the general adequacy of a wave field to describe a state of affairs, underlies the description of both the object and the instrument of observation, these examples only illustrate and make vivid what must generally be true: the universal limitation, in contrast to classical physics, of the extent to which all aspects of a physical system can be defined for the same system in the same instance.

In observing atomic systems, in observing a system where the finiteness of the quantum of action plays an important part, we have a wide range of choice in the kind of probe, the kind of experiment, the kind of experimental equipment we wish to make. To any of these, if it is a good experiment, there will be a meaningful answer which tells us what the state of affairs is. From this, and from the wave field which represents it, we can then make statistical predictions of what will happen in a subsequent experiment. The potentialities of measurement are varied. We can do one thing or another; there are no inherent limits on the choice of actions on the part of the observer.

This is a very different view of reality from Newton's giant machine. It is not causal; there is no complete causal determination of the future on the basis of available knowledge of the present. The application of the laws of quantum theory restricts, but does not in general define, the outcome of an experiment. This means that every observation on a system reveals some new knowledge as to what its state is that did not exist before, and could not by analysis and mathematical computation have been obtained. It means that every intervention to make a measurement, to study what is going on in the atomic world, creates, despite all the universal order of this world, a new, a unique, not fully predictable, situation.

Even in a brief account other points need to be mentioned. We have almost lost the concept of equations of motion, having discovered that the very terms in which they are formulated—position, velocity, acceleration, and force—are not simultaneously applicable and do not, taken together, correspond to things that we know about the electron with enough accuracy to be meaningful for an atomic system. Instead, what we can have is a knowledge of the state, summarizing for us what we have found by observation; and the analogue of the equation of motion must tell us how, in response to forces acting within the system or upon it, this state will change with time. This, it turns out, is just what Schroedinger's equation does. And once again this equation, when applied to the familiar contexts of massive bodies and great distances, where the quantum of action is in fact negligibly small, will describe for us waves so reasonably concentrated in space, so little dispersed about their average wave length, that the Newtonian orbit reappears in its unaltered, classical path.

But this condition—this emergence of an orbit—is a long way from the wave that describes the normal state of an atom. State and orbit, like position and impulse, are complementary notions; where one applies, the other can-

not be defined, and for a full description we must be able
to use now one, now the other, depending on the observation and the questions that we put.

When we speak here of observer and object, of instrument or probe, and system to be probed, we are not talking of the mind of man. We are talking of a division
between the object of study and the means used to study
it. That division can be made in more than one way. We
may regard the a-particles that Rutherford used as an instrument, and their response as a measure of the state of
affairs. We may regard the a-particle as a part of the system we are studying, and the slits that define its path or
the fields that deflect it and the screens that detect it as the
instrument. But whichever we do, the observation will always be transformed into some large-scale happening—
some flash of light, some triggering of a circuit, some
pointing of a pointer on the dial of an instrument—which
is well defined and familiar and unambiguous, and where
the question of our freedom to do one or another observation on it no longer is relevant. The atomic world has not
lost its objective quality; but it attains this by means of
those interlockings with experiment which we use to define
one or another of its properties and to measure them.

It needs to be clear that what is described here is
not an expression of mood or preference or taste; it is
an exact, beautiful, quantitative, immensely versatile,
and immensely successful science. It is what students
learn when they prepare themselves for further re-
searches in physics, or what engineers learn whose

engineering involves a knowledge of the solid state of physical materials, or what chemists learn if they wish to understand the subtler features of chemical bonding or chemical kinetics, or astronomers if they wish to know what things are like in the interior of the stars. One could go much farther in describing this discipline, even without mathematics; but the words would before long become cumbersome and unfamiliar and almost a misinterpretation of what in mathematical terms can be said with beauty and simplicity.

Even some of the more paradoxical features of quantum theory turn out to be related to practical matters of real importance. One of the earliest to be noted and the oddest is this: if, in familiar life, we roll a ball up a hill and it does not have enough vigor to get over the top, it will roll back on the same side; it will not get through the hill. But if we bombard such a hill with α-particles or electrons they may have a small chance of getting through, even when they cannot get over. This has a close analogy with the fact that very small objects do not cast sharp shadows in a beam of light. Light because of its wave nature bends around them. It corresponds to the fact that when we let electrons or other particles of definite energy encounter a barrier, neither the kinetic nor the potential energy alone can be completely well defined; and indeed, were we to try to detect the electron just as it passes through the hill, we should need an experiment that could give the electron enough energy to be quite legitimately on top of the hill. This penetration of barriers is not without importance. It accounts for the fact that the α-particles that Rutherford used could sometimes, after millions of years, escape from the nuclei through a high hill where electrostatic repulsion had imprisoned them. It accounts for the fact that in the sun and other stars nuclei having only very moderate energy occasionally come into contact and react. Thus the stars light the heavens, and the sun warms and nourishes the earth.

Another consequence of the wave-like character of all matter is that, when particles with very low velocity and very long wave length bombard other particles of matter, they may interact far more often than if these interactions were limited to their coming in contact. The very lack of definition of their relative position makes interaction possible, in some cases over distances characterized not by their dimensions but by their wave length. This is the circumstance which, among many others, enables the rare Uranium-235, as it occurs in natural uranium, to catch up enough of the neutrons which fly about to sustain a chain reaction in an atomic reactor.

There are even some odd things about the identity and the identifiability of the electrons themselves. That they are all similar we know. Their inherent properties, their charge, their mass when at rest, are the same. We wish that we understood this better; some day, no doubt, we shall; but we know that it is true. But if classical physics were the whole story, we could still, if we wished, always identify an electron, and know that it was the same as the one we had seen before. We could follow it, not, it is true, without trouble, but without paradox, without inconsistency, from where we first found it through its collisions and interactions and deflections and changes by keeping in touch with its trajectory. If it hit another electron, we would know which it was that came out in one direction and which in another. In fact this is not really true, except in those special instances where the collision is of such low energy that the two electrons can be described by waves which never overlap at the same place at the same time. As soon as that is no longer the case, we lose in principle all ability to tell one electron from another; and in atomic physics, where the electrons of an atom, and even the electrons of neighboring atoms, are not well defined in position and can often occupy the same volume, we have no way of identifying the individual particle. This, too, has consequences. When two electrons collide, the wave that represents one of them and the wave that represents the other may, and do, interfere; and this gives rise to novel effects and new forms for the interactions produced by their electric repulsion. It is responsible for the permanent magnetism of magnets. It is responsible for the bonding of organic chemistry and for the very existence in any form that we can readily imagine of living matter and of life itself.

These examples are not given to perplex and bemuse. They are rather illustrations of how even the most paradoxical and unexpected consequences of the new mechanics, of wave-particle duality, and of complementarity are involved in an understanding of important and familiar features of the natural world, and of how massive is the system of understanding and knowledge of which they are a part.

5.

UNCOMMON SENSE

A CENTURY after Newton, in 1784, the progress of that century was celebrated in an anonymous memorial lodged in the ball of the tower of St. Margaret's church at Gotha, to be found by men of future times. It read:

"Our days have been the happiest time of the eighteenth century. . . . Hatred born of dogma and the compulsion of conscience sink away; love of man and freedom of thought gain the upper hand. The arts and sciences blossom, and our vision into the workshop of nature goes deep. Artisans approach artists in perfection; useful skills flower at all levels. Here you have a faithful portrait of our time. . . . Do the same for those who come after you and rejoice!"

Transience is the backdrop for the play of human progress, for the improvement of man, the growth of his knowledge, the increase of his power, his corruption and his partial redemption. Our civilizations perish; the carved stone, the written word, the heroic act fade into a memory of memory and in the end are gone. The day will come when our race is gone; this house, this earth in which we live will one day be unfit for human habitation, as the sun ages and alters.

Yet no man, be he agnostic or Buddhist or Christian, thinks wholly in these terms. His acts, his thoughts, what he sees of the world around him—the falling of a leaf or a child's joke or the rise of the moon—are part of history; but they are not only part of history; they are a part of becoming and of process but not only that: they partake also of the world outside of time; they partake of the light of eternity.

These two ways of thinking, the way of time and history and the way of eternity and of timelessness, are both part of man's effort to comprehend the world in which he lives. Neither is comprehended in the other nor reducible to it. They are, as we have learned to say in physics, complementary views, each supplementing the other, neither telling the whole story. Let us return to this.

First, we had best review and extend somewhat this account of the complementarity of the physicists. In its simplest form it is that an electron must sometimes be considered as a wave, and sometimes as a particle—a wave, that is, with the continuous propagation and characteristic interference that we learn to understand in the optics laboratory, or as a particle, a thing with well-defined location at any time, discrete and individual and atomic. There is this same duality for all matter and for light. In a little subtler form this complementarity means that there are situations in which the position of an atomic object can be measured and defined and thought about without contradiction; and other situations in which this is not so, but in which other qualities, such as the energy or the impulse of the system, are defined and meaningful. The more nearly appropriate the first way of thinking is to a situation, the more wholly inappropriate the second, so that there are in fact no atomic situations in which both impulse and position will be defined well enough to permit the sort of prediction with which Newtonian mechanics has familiarized us.

It is not only that when we have made an observation on a system and determined, let us say, its position, we do not know its impulse. That is true, but more than that is true. We could say that we know the position of that system and that it may have any one of a number of different impulses. If we try on that basis to predict its behavior as a sort of average behavior of all objects which have the measured position and which have different and unmeasured impulses, and work out the average answer according to Newton's laws, we get a result that is wholly at variance with what we find in nature. This is because of the peculiar property, which has no analogue in the mechanics of large objects, of interference between waves representing the consequences of assuming one impulse and those of assuming another. We are not, that is, allowed to suppose that position and velocity are attributes of an atomic system, some of which we know and others of which we might know but do not. We have to recognize that the attempt to discover these unknown attributes would lose for us the known; that we have a choice, a disjunction; and that this corresponds to the different ways we can go about observing our atom or experimenting with it.

We have a state of affairs completely defined by the nature of the observation and by its outcome—the nature determining what properties of the system will be well defined in the state and what poorly. The outcome then is the determination of the well-defined quantities by measurement. This state thus is a summary, symbolic and uncomfortably abstract for general exposition, of what sort of observation we have made and what we have found through it. It codifies those characteristics of the experimental arrangement which are reliable, in the sense that the equipment we use records something that we know about atomic systems. It describes also those characteristics that are indeterminate, in the sense that they may not only have been disturbed or altered, but that their disturbance cannot be registered or controlled without the loss, in the experiment, of all ability to measure what was supposed to be measured.

This state, this description of the atom, is not the only way of talking about it. It is the only way appropriate to the information we have and the means that we have used to obtain it. It is the full account of this information; and if the experiment was properly and scrupulously done it tells us all that we can find out. It is not all that we could have found out had we chosen a different experiment. It is all that we could find out having chosen this.

This state is objective. We can calculate its properties, reproduce it with similar atoms on another occasion, verify its properties and its ways of change with time. There is no element of the arbitrary or subjective. Once we have done our experiment and its result is recorded and the atom disengaged, we know its meaning and its outcome; we can then forget the details of how we got our information.

But, although the state of the system is objective, a mechanical picture of how it was brought into being is not generally possible. There is a most vivid example of this, made famous by the prominent part it played in the debates between Einstein and Bohr as to the meaning and adequacy of atomic theory. It can be put rather simply. Let us suppose that we have two objects; one of them may be an electron or an atom, and it will be the one we wish to study. The other may be a relatively large piece of matter—a screen with a hole through it, or any other body; but it should be heavy so that its motion will be unimportant compared to that of the electron. Let us suppose that we by measurement know the impulse or momentum of both of these objects, and have them collide. Let the electron go through the hole, or bounce off the other body. If, after the collision, we measure the impulse of the heavy body, we will then know that of the electron because, as Newton's third law teaches us, the sum of the impulses is not altered by the collision. In that case we would have a state of the electron of well-defined impulse, as precisely defined as we had made the precision of our measurements. If, on the other hand, we observed the position of the heavy body, we would know where the light one had been at the moment of the collision, and so would have a quite different description of its state, one in which its position and not its impulse had been well defined—or, in the language of waves, a spherical wave with its center at the point of collision, and not a plane wave with its direction and wave length corresponding to the momentum.

We have thus the option of realizing one or the other of two wholly dissimilar states for the electron, by a choice of what we observe about the heavy body with which it once was in interaction. We are not, in any meaningful sense, physically altering or qualifying the electron; we are defining a part of, although in this case a late part of, the experimental procedure, the very nature of the experiment itself. If we exercise neither option, if we let the heavy body go with unmeasured momentum and undefined position, then we know nothing of the electron at all. It has no state, and we are not prepared to make any meaningful predictions of what will become of it or of what we shall find should we again attempt an experiment upon it. The electron cannot be objectified in a manner independent of the means chosen for observing or studying it. The only property we can ascribe to it without such consideration is our total ignorance.

This is a sharp reminder that ways of thinking about

things, which seem natural and inevitable and almost appear not to rest on experience so much as on the inherent qualities of thought and nature, do in fact rest on experience; and that there are parts of experience rendered accessible by exploration and experimental refinement where these ways of thought no longer apply.

It is important to remember that, if a very much subtler view of the properties of an electron in an atomic system is necessary to describe the wealth of experience we have had with such systems, it all rests on accepting without revision the traditional accounts of the behavior of large-scale objects. The measurements that we have talked about in such highly abstract form do in fact come down in the end to looking at the position of a pointer, or the reading of time on a watch, or measuring out where on a photographic plate or a phosphorescent screen a flash of light or a patch of darkness occurs. They all rest on reducing the experience with atomic systems to experiment and observation made manifest, unambiguous, and objective in the behavior of large objects, where the precautions and incertitudes of the atomic domain no longer directly apply. So it is that ever-increasing refinements and critical revisions in the way we talk about remote or small or inaccessible parts of the physical world have no direct relevance to the familiar physical world of common experience.

Common sense is not wrong in the view that it is meaningful, appropriate, and necessary to talk about the large objects of our daily experience as though they had a velocity that we knew, and a place that we knew, and all the rest of it. Common sense is wrong only if it insists that what is familiar must reappear in what is unfamiliar. It is wrong only if it leads us to expect that every country that we visit is like the last country we saw. Common sense, as the common heritage from the millennia of common life, may lead us into error if we wholly forget the circumstances to which that common life has been restricted.

Misunderstanding of these relations has led men to wish to draw from new discoveries, and particularly those in the atomic domain, far-reaching consequences for the ordinary affairs of men. Thus it was noted that, since the ultimate laws of atomic behavior are not strictly causal, not strictly determinate, the famous argument of Laplace for a wholly determinate universe could not be maintained. And there were men who believed that they had discovered in the acausal and indeterminate character of atomic events the physical basis for that sense of freedom which characterizes man's behavior in the face of decision and of responsibility.

In a similar light-hearted way it was pointed out that, as the state of an atomic system requires observation for its definition, so the course of psychological phenomena might be irretrievably altered by the very effort to probe them—as a man's thoughts are altered by the fact that he has formulated and spoken them. It is, of course, not the fact that observation may change the state of an atomic system that gives rise to the need for a complementary description; it is the fact that, if the observation is to be meaningful, it will preclude any analysis or control of that change, that is decisive.

But these misapplications of the findings of atomic physics to human affairs do not establish that there are no valid analogies. These analogies will, in the nature of things, be less sharp, less compelling, less ingenious. They will rest upon the fact that complementary modes of thought and complementary descriptions of reality are an old, long-enduring part of our tradition. All that the experience of atomic physics can do in these affairs is to give us a reminder, and a certain reassurance, that these ways of talking and thinking can be factual, appropriate, precise, and free of obscurantism.

There are a number of examples which are illuminated by, and in turn illuminate, the complementarity of atomic theory. Some of them are from quite different parts of human life and some of them from older parts of science. There is one from physics itself which is revealing, both in its analogies and its points of difference. One of the great triumphs of nineteenth-century physics was the kinetic theory of heat—what is called statistical mechanics. This is both an interpretation and a deduction of many of the large-scale properties and tendencies of matter: of the tendency, for instance, of bodies that can exchange heat to come to a common temperature, or of the density of a gas to be uniform throughout a container, or of work to dissipate itself in heat, or quite generally of all of those irreversible processes in nature wherein the entropy of systems increases, and forms become more uniform and less differentiated when left to themselves to develop.

The phenomena we deal with here are defined in terms of temperature and density and pressure and other large-scale properties. The kinetic theory, statistical mechanics, interprets the behavior of these systems in terms of the forces acting on the molecules and of the motion of the molecules that compose them, which are usually quite accurately described by Newton's laws. But it is a statistical theory of this motion, recognizing that in fact we do not in general know, and are not in detail concerned with, the positions and velocities of the molecules themselves, but only with their average behavior. We interpret the temperature of a gas, for instance, in terms of the average kinetic energy of its molecules, and the pressure as the average of the forces exerted by the collision of these molecules on the surface of the container. This description in terms of averages, embodying as part of itself our ignorance of the detailed state of affairs, is thus in some sense complementary to a complete dynamic description in terms of the motion of the individual molecules. In this sense kinetic theory and dynamics are complementary. One applies to a situation in which the individual patterns of molecular behavior are known and studied; the other applies to a situation largely defined by our ignorance of these patterns.

But the analogy to atomic complementarity is only partial, because there is nothing in the classical dynamics which underlies kinetic theory to suggest that the behavior of a gas would be any different if we had performed the immense job of locating and measuring what all the molecules were doing. We might then, it is true, not find it natural to talk about temperature, because we would need no average behavior; we would have an actual one; but we could still define the temperature in terms of the total kinetic energy of the molecules, and we would still find that it tended to equalize between one part of the system and another.

We have therefore a situation in which there are two ways of describing a system, two sets of concepts, two centers of preoccupation. One is appropriate when we are dealing with a very few molecules and want to know what those molecules do; the other appropriate when we have a large mass of matter and only rough and large-scale observations about it.

There is, however, no logical or inherent difficulty within the framework of classical physics, in combining both descriptions for a single system—and classical physics, we repeat, is adequate for most, if not all, of these problems of statistical mechanics. It is not that we cannot do this without violating the laws of physics; it is that it makes no sense to do it, since each description is appropriate to a context quite different from the other. It is clear that, if we insisted on the detailed description of the motion of individual molecules, the notions of probability which turn out to be so essential for our understanding of the irreversible character of physical events in nature would never enter. We should not have the great insight that we now do: namely, that the direction of change in the world is from the less probable to the more, from the more organized to the less, because all we would be talking about would be an incredible number of orbits and trajectories and collisions. It would be a great miracle to us that, out of equations of motion, which to every allowed motion permit a precisely opposite one, we could nevertheless emerge into a world in which there is a trend of change with time which is irreversible, unmistakable, and familiar in all our physical experience.

In considering the relations between the various sciences, there are similar instances of complementary views. In many cases, it is not clear whether this is the sort of complementarity that we have between the statistical and dynamic descriptions of a gas, a contrast of interest and terminology, but not an inherent inapplicability of two ways of talking; or whether on the contrary the situation is in fact more as it is in atomic physics, where the nature of the world is such that the two modes of description cannot be applied at once to the same situation. Every science has its own language. But dictionaries of translation between the languages do exist, and mark an ever-growing understanding and unity of science as a whole. It is not always clear whether the dictionaries will be complete; between physics and chemistry they apparently are. Everything the chemist observes and describes can be talked about in terms of atomic mechanics, and most of it at least can be understood. Yet no one suggests that, in dealing with the complex chemical forms which are of biological interest, the language of atomic physics would be helpful. Rather it would tend to obscure the great regularities of biochemistry, as the dynamic description of a gas would obscure its thermodynamic behavior.

The contrast becomes even more marked when we consider the physico-chemical description of living forms. Here, in spite of the miraculous sharpness of the tools of chemical analysis, of the extensive use not only of the microscope but of the electron microscope to determine fine details of biological structure, in spite of the use of tracers to follow changes on a molecular scale, questions have still been raised as to whether this description can in the nature of things be complete.

The question involves two points: the first having to do with the impossibility of wholly isolating a biological system from its physical environment without killing it; the second with the possibility that a really complete physico-chemical study of the pivotal structures in biological processes—of genes, let us say, in the nuclei of dividing cells —might not be incompatible with the undisturbed course of life itself. It would appear to be the general opinion of biologists that no such limitations will prove decisive; that a complete description of biology will be possible not only in terms of the concepts of biology but in terms reducible to those of physics and chemistry. Certainly it is a large part of the aim and wonder of biological progress to carry this program as far as possible.

Analogous questions appear much sharper, and their answer more uncertain, when we think of the phenomena of consciousness; and, despite all the progress that has been made in the physiology of the sense organs and of the brain, despite our increasing knowledge of these intricate marvels both as to their structure and their functioning, it seems rather unlikely that we shall be able to describe in physico-chemical terms the physiological phenomena which accompany a conscious thought, or sentiment, or will. Today the outcome is uncertain. Whatever the outcome, we know that, should an understanding of the physical correlate of elements of consciousness indeed be available, it will not itself be the appropriate description for the thinking man himself, for the clarification of his thoughts, the resolution of his will, or the delight of his eye and mind at works of beauty. Indeed, an understanding of the complementary nature of conscious life and its physical interpretation appears to me a lasting element in human understanding and a proper formulation of the historic views called psycho-physical parallelism.

For within conscious life, and in its relations with the description of the physical world, there are again many examples. There is the relation between the cognitive and the affective sides of our lives, between knowledge or analysis and emotion or feeling. There is the relation between the aesthetic and the heroic, between feeling and that precursor and definer of action, the ethical commitment; there is the classical relation between the analysis of one's self, the determination of one's motives and purposes, and that freedom of choice, that freedom of decision and action, which are complementary to it.

Whether a physico-chemical description of the material counterpart of consciousness will in fact ever be possible, whether physiological or psychological observation will ever permit with any relevant confidence the prediction of our behavior in moments of decision and in moments of challenge, we may be sure that these analyses and these understandings, even should they exist, will be as irrelevant to the acts of decision and the castings of the will as are the trajectories of molecules to the entropy of a gas. To be touched with awe, or humor, to be moved by beauty, to make a commitment or a determination, to understand some truth—these are complementary modes of the human spirit. All of them are part of man's spiritual life. None can replace the others, and where one is called for the others are in abeyance.

Just as with the α-particles of Rutherford, which were first for him an object of study and then became for him a tool of study, a tool for investigating other objects, so our thoughts and words can be the subject of reflection and analysis; so we can be introspective, critical, and full of doubt. And so, in other times and other contexts, these same words, these same thoughts taken as instruments, are the power of human understanding itself, and the means of our further enlightenment.

The wealth and variety of physics itself, the greater wealth and variety of the natural sciences taken as a whole, the more familiar, yet still strange and far wider wealth of the life of the human spirit, enriched by complementary, not at once compatible ways, irreducible one to the other, have a greater harmony. They are the elements of man's sorrow and his splendor, his frailty and his power, his death, his passing, and his undying deeds.

6.

THE SCIENCES
AND MAN'S COMMUNITY

FOR some moments during these lectures we have looked together into one of the rooms of the house called "science." This is a relatively quiet room that we know as quantum theory or atomic theory. The great girders which frame it, the lights and shadows and vast windows—these were the work of a generation our predecessor more than two decades ago. It is not wholly quiet. Young people visit it and study in it and pass on to other chambers; and from time to time someone rearranges a piece of the furniture to make the whole more harmonious; and many, as we have done, peer through its windows or walk through it as sight-seers. It is not so old but that one can hear the sound of the new wings being built nearby, where men walk high in the air to erect new scaffoldings, not unconscious of how far they may fall. All about there are busy workshops where the builders are active, and very near indeed are those of us who, learning more of the primordial structure of matter, hope some day for chambers as fair and lovely as that in which we have spent the years of our youth and our prime.

It is a vast house indeed. It does not appear to have been built upon any plan but to have grown as a great city grows. There is no central chamber, no one corridor from which all others debouch. All about the periphery men are at work studying the vast reaches of space and the state of affairs billions of years ago; studying the intricate and subtle but wonderfully meet mechanisms by which life proliferates, alters, and endures; studying the reach of the mind and its ways of learning; digging deep into the atoms and the atoms within atoms and their unfathomed order. It is a house so vast that none of us know it, and even the most fortunate have seen most rooms only from the outside or by a fleeting passage, as in a king's palace open to visitors. It is a house so vast that there is not and need not be complete concurrence on where its chambers stop and those of the neighboring mansions begin.

It is not arranged in a line nor a square nor a circle nor a pyramid, but with a wonderful randomness suggestive of unending growth and improvisation. Not many people live in the house, relatively speaking—perhaps if we count all its chambers and take residence requirements quite lightly, one tenth of one per cent, of all the people in this world—probably, by any reasonable definition, far fewer. And even those who live here live elsewhere also, live in houses where the rooms are not labelled atomic theory or genetics or the internal constitution of the stars, but quite different names like power and production and evil and beauty and history and children and the word of God.

We go in and out; even the most assiduous of us is not bound to this vast structure. One thing we find throughout the house: there are no locks; there are no shut doors; wherever we go there are the signs and usually the words of welcome. It is an open house, open to all comers.

The discoveries of science, the new rooms in this great house, have changed the way men think of things outside its walls. We have some glimmering now of the depth in time and the vastness in space of the physical world we live in. An awareness of how long our history and how immense our cosmos touches us even in simple earthly deliberations. We have learned from the natural history of the earth and from the story of evolution to have a sense of history, of time and change. We learn to talk of ourselves, and of the nature of the world and its reality as not wholly fixed in a silent quiet moment, but as unfolding with novelty and alteration, decay and new growth. We have understood something of the inner harmony and beauty of strange primitive cultures, and through this see the qualities of our own life in an altered perspective, and recognize its accidents as well as its inherent necessities. We are, I should think, not patriots less but patriots very differently for loving what is ours and understanding a little of the love of others for their lands and ways. We have begun to understand that it is not only in his rational life that man's psyche is intelligible, that even in what may appear to be his least rational actions and sentiments we may discover a new order. We have the beginnings of an understanding of what it is in man, and more in simple organisms, that is truly heritable, and rudimentary clues as to how the inheritance occurs. We know, in surprising detail, what is the physical counterpart of the act of vision and of other modes of perception. Not one of these new ideas and new insights is so little, or has so short a reach in its bearing on the common understanding but that it alone could make a proper theme for "Science and the Common Understanding." Yet we have been, bearing in mind my limited area of experience, in that one room of the part of the house where physics is, in which I have for some years worked and taught.

In that one room—in that relatively quiet room where we have been together—we have found things quite strange for those who have not been there before, yet reminiscent of what we have seen in other houses and known in other days. We have seen that in the atomic world we have been led by experience to use descriptions and ideas that apply to the large-scale world of matter, to the familiar world of our schoolday physics; ideas like the position of a body and its acceleration and its impulse and the forces acting on it; ideas like wave and interference; ideas like cause and probability. But what is new, what was not anticipated a half-century ago, is that, though to an atomic system there is a potential applicability of one or another of these ideas, in any real situation only some of these ways of description can be actual. This is because we need to take into account not merely the atomic system we are studying, but the means we use in observing it, and the fitness of these experimental means for defining and measuring selected properties of the system. All such ways of observing are needed for the whole experience of the atomic world; all but one are excluded in any actual experience. In the specific instance, there is a proper and consistent way to describe what the experience is; what it implies; what it predicts and thus how to deal with its consequences. But any such specific instance excludes by its existence the application of other ideas, other modes of prediction, other consequences. They are, we say, complementary to one another; atomic theory is in part an account of these descriptions and in part an understanding of the circumstances to which one applies, or another or another.

And so it is with man's life. He may be any of a number of things; he will not be all of them. He may be well versed, he may be a poet, he may be a creator in one or more than one science; he will not be all kinds of man or all kinds of scientist; and he will be lucky if he has a bit of familiarity outside the room in which he works.

So it is with the great antinomies that through the ages have organized and yet disunited man's experience: the antinomy between the ceaseless change and wonderful novelty and the perishing of all earthly things, and the eternity which inheres in every happening; in the antinomy between growth and order, between the spontaneous and changing and irregular and the symmetrical and balanced; in the related antinomy between freedom and necessity; between action, the life of the will, and observation and analysis and the life of reason; between the question "how?" and the questions "why?" and "to what end?"; between the causes that derive from natural law, from unvarying regularities in the natural world, and those other causes that express purposes and define goals and ends.

So it is in the antinomy between the individual and the community; man who is an end in himself and man whose tradition, whose culture, whose works, whose words have meaning in terms of other men and his relations to them. All our experience has shown that we can neither think, nor in any true sense live, without reference to these antinomic modes. We cannot in any sense be both the observers and the actors in any specific instance, or we shall fail properly to be either one or the other; yet we know that our life is built of these two modes, is part free and part inevitable, is part creation and part discipline, is part acceptance and part effort. We have no written rules that assign us to these ways; but we know that only folly and death of the spirit results when we deny one or the other, when we erect one as total and absolute and make the others derivative and secondary. We recognize this when we live as men. We talk to one another; we philosophize; we admire great men and their moments of greatness; we read; we study; we recognize and love in a particular act that happy union of the generally incompatible. With all of this we learn to use some reasonable part of the full register of man's resources.

We are, of course, an ignorant lot; even the best of us knows how to do only a very few things well; and of what is available in knowledge of fact, whether of science or of history, only the smallest part is in any one man's knowing.

The greatest of the changes that science has brought is the acuity of change; the greatest novelty the extent of novelty. Short of rare times of great disaster, civilizations have not known such rapid alteration in the conditions of their life, such rapid flowering of many varied sciences, such rapid changes in the ideas we have about the world and one another. What has been true in the days of a great disaster or great military defeat for one people at one time is true for all of us now, in the sense that our ends have little in common with our beginnings. Within a lifetime what we learned at school has been rendered inadequate by new discoveries and new inventions; the ways that we learn in childhood are only very meagerly adequate to the issues that we must meet in maturity.

In fact, of course, the notion of universal knowledge has always been an illusion; but it is an illusion fostered by the monistic view of the world in which a few great central truths determine in all its wonderful and amazing proliferation everything else that is true. We are not today tempted to search for these keys that unlock the whole of human knowledge and of man's experience. We know that we are ignorant; we are well taught it, and the more surely and deeply we know our own job the better able we are to appreciate the full measure of our pervasive ignorance. We know that these are inherent limits, compounded, no doubt, and exaggerated by that sloth and that complacency without which we would not be men at all.

But knowledge rests on knowledge; what is new is meaningful because it departs slightly from what was known before; this is a world of frontiers, where even the liveliest of actors or observers will be absent most of the time from most of them. Perhaps this sense was not so sharp in the village—that village which we have learned a little about but probably do not understand too well—the village of slow change and isolation and fixed culture which evokes our nostalgia even if not our full comprehension. Perhaps in the villages men were not so lonely; perhaps they found in each other a fixed community, a fixed and only slowly growing store of knowledge—a single world. Even that we may doubt, for there seem to be always in the culture of such times and places vast domains of mystery, if not unknowable, then imperfectly known, endless and open.

As for ourselves in these times of change, of ever-increasing knowledge, of collective power and individual impotence, of heroism and of drudgery, of progress and of tragedy, we too are brothers. And if we, who are the inheritors of two millennia of Christian tradition, understand that for us we have come to be brothers second by being children first, we know that in vast parts of the world where there has been no Christian tradition, and with men who never have been and never may be Christian in faith there is nevertheless a bond of brotherhood. We know this not only because of the almost universal ideal of human brotherhood and human community; we know it at first hand from the more modest, more diverse, more fleeting associations which are the substance of our life. The ideal of brotherhood, the ideal of fraternity in which all men, wicked and virtuous, wretched and fortunate, are banded together has its counterpart in the experience of communities, not ideal, not universal, imperfect, impermanent, as different from the ideal and as reminiscent of it as are the ramified branches of science from the ideal of a unitary, all-encompassing science of the eighteenth century.

Each of us knows from his own life how much even a casual and limited association of men goes beyond him in knowledge, in understanding, in humanity, and in power. Each of us, from a friend or a book or by concerting of the little we know with what others know, has broken the iron circle of his frustration. Each of us has asked help and been given it, and within our measure each of us has offered it. Each of us knows the great new freedom sensed almost as a miracle, that men banded together for some finite purpose experience from the power of their common effort. We are likely to remember the times of the last war, where the common danger brought forth in soldier, in worker, in scientist, and engineer a host of new experiences of the power and the comfort in even bleak undertakings, of common, concerted, co-operative life. Each of us knows how much he has been transcended by the group of which he has been or is a part; each of us has felt the solace of other men's knowledge to stay his own ignorance, of other men's wisdom to stay his folly, of other men's courage to answer his doubts or his weakness.

These are the fluid communities, some of long duration when circumstances favored—like the political party or many a trade union—some fleeting and vivid, encompassing in the time of their duration a moment only of the member's life; and in our world at least they are ramified and improvised, living and dying, growing and falling off almost as a form of life itself. This may be more true of the United States than of any other country. Certainly the bizarre and comical aspects impressed de Tocqueville more than a century ago when he visited our land and commented on the readiness with which men would band together: to improve the planting of a town, or for political reform, or for the pursuit or inter-exchange of knowledge, or just for the sake of banding together, because they liked one another or disliked someone else. Circumstances may have exaggerated the role of the societies, of the fluid and yet intense communities in the United States; yet these form a common pattern for our civilization. It brought men together in the Royal Society and in the French Academy and in the Philosophical Society that Franklin founded, in family, in platoon, on a ship, in the laboratory, in almost everything but a really proper club.

If we err today—and I think we do—it is in expecting too much of knowledge from the individual and too much of synthesis from the community. We tend to think of these communities, no less than of the larger brotherhood of man, as made up of individuals, as composed of them as an atom is of its ingredients. We think similarly of general laws and broad ideas as made up of the instances which illustrate them, and from an observation of which we may have learned them.

Yet this is not the whole. The individual event, the act, goes far beyond the general law. It is a sort of intersection of many generalities, harmonizing them in one instance as they cannot be harmonized in general. And we as men are not only the ingredients of our communities; we are their intersection, making a harmony which does not exist between the communities except as we, the individual men, may create it and reveal it. So much of what we think, our acts, our judgments of beauty and of right and wrong, come to us from our fellow men that what would be left were we to take all this away would be neither recognizable nor human. We are men because we are part of, but not because only part of, communities; and the attempt to understand man's brotherhood in terms only of the individual man is as little likely to describe our world as is the attempt to describe general laws as the summary of their instances. These are indeed two complementary views, neither reducible to the other, no more reducible than is the electron as wave to the electron as particle.

And this is the mitigant of our ignorance. It is true that

none of us will know very much; and most of us will see
the end of our days without understanding in all its detail
and beauty the wonders uncovered even in a single branch
of a single science. Most of us will not even know, as a
member of any intimate circle, anyone who has such
knowledge; but it is also true that, although we are sure
not to know everything and rather likely not to know very
much, we can know anything that is known to man, and
may, with luck and sweat, even find out some things that
have not before been known to him. This possibility,
which, as a universal condition of man's life is new, represents today a high and determined hope, not yet a reality;
it is for us in England and in the United States not wholly
remote or unfamiliar. It is one of the manifestations of our
belief in equality, that belief which could perhaps better
be described as a commitment to unparalleled diversity
and unevenness in the distribution of attainments, knowledge, talent, and power.

This open access to knowledge, these unlocked doors
and signs of welcome, are a mark of a freedom as fundamental as any. They give a freedom to resolve difference
by converse, and, where converse does not unite, to let
tolerance compose diversity. This would appear to be a
freedom barely compatible with modern political tyranny.
The multitude of communities, the free association for
converse or for common purpose, are acts of creation. It
is not merely that without them the individual is the
poorer; without them a part of human life, not more nor
less fundamental than the individual, is foreclosed. It is a

cruel and humorless sort of pun that so powerful a present form of modern tyranny should call itself by the very name of a belief in community, by a word "communism" which in other times evoked memories of villages and village inns and of artisans concerting their skills, and of men of learning content with anonymity. But perhaps only a malignant end can follow the systematic belief that all communities are one community; that all truth is one truth; that all experience is compatible with all other; that total knowledge is possible; that all that is potential can exist as actual. This is not man's fate; this is not his path; to force him on it makes him resemble not that divine image of the all-knowing and all-powerful but the helpless, iron-bound prisoner of a dying world. The open society, the unrestricted access to knowledge, the unplanned and uninhibited association of men for its furtherance—these are what may make a vast, complex, evergrowing, ever-changing, ever more specialized and expert technological world nevertheless a world of human community.

So it is with the unity of science—that unity that is far more a unity of comparable dedication than a unity of common total understanding. This heartening phrase, "the unity of science," often tends to evoke a wholly false picture, a picture of a few basic truths, a few critical techniques, methods, and ideas, from which all discoveries and understanding of science derive; a sort of central exchange, access to which will illuminate the atoms and the galaxies, the genes and the sense organs. The unity of science is based rather on just such a community as I have described. All parts of it are open to all of us, and this is no merely formal invitation. The history of science is rich in example of the fruitfulness of bringing two sets of techniques, two sets of ideas, developed in separate contexts for the pursuit of new truth, into touch with one another. The sciences fertilize each other; they grow by contact and by common enterprise. Once again, this means that the scientist may profit from learning about any other science; it does not mean that he must learn about them all. It means that the unity is a potential unity, the unity of the things that might be brought together and might throw light one on the other. It is not global or total or hierarchical.

Even in science, and even without visiting the room in its house called atomic theory, we are again and again reminded of the complementary traits in our own life, even in our own professional life. We are nothing without the work of others our predecessors, others our teachers, others our contemporaries. Even when, in the measure of our adequacy and our fullness, new insight and new order are created, we are still nothing without others. Yet we are more.

There is a similar duality in our relations to wider society. For society our work means many things: pleasure, we hope, for those who follow it; instruction for those who perhaps need it; but also and far more widely, it means a common power, a power to achieve that which could not be achieved without knowledge. It means the cure of illness and the alleviation of suffering; it means the easing of labor and the widening of the readily accessible frontiers of experience, of communication, and of instruction. It means, in an earthy way, the power of betterment—that riddled word. We are today anxiously aware that the power to change is not always necessarily good.

As new instruments of war, of newly massive terror, add to the ferocity and totality of warfare, we understand that it is a special mark and problem of our age that man's ever-present preoccupation with improving his lot, with alleviating hunger and poverty and exploitation, must be brought into harmony with the over-riding need to limit and largely to eliminate resort to organized violence between nation and nation. The increasingly expert destruction of man's spirit by the power of police, more wicked if not more awful than the ravages of nature's own hand, is another such power, good only if never to be used.

We regard it as proper and just that the patronage of science by society is in large measure based on the increased power which knowledge gives. If we are anxious that the power so given and so obtained be used with wisdom and with love of humanity, that is an anxiety we share with almost everyone. But we also know how little of the deep new knowledge which has altered the face of the world, which has changed—and increasingly and ever more profoundly must change—man's views of the world, resulted from a quest for practical ends or an interest in exercising the power that knowledge gives. For most of us, in most of those moments when we were most free of corruption, it has been the beauty of the world of nature and the strange and compelling harmony of its order, that has sustained, inspirited, and led us. That also is as it should be. And if the forms in which society provides and exercises its patronage leave these incentives strong and secure, new knowledge will never stop as long as there are men.

We know that our work is rightly both an instrument and an end. A great discovery is a thing of beauty; and our faith—our binding, quiet faith—is that knowledge is good and good in itself. It is also an instrument; it is an instrument for our successors, who will use it to probe elsewhere and more deeply; it is an instrument for technology, for the practical arts, and for man's affairs. So it is with us as scientists; so it is with us as men. We are at once instrument and end, discoverers and teachers, actors and observers. We understand, as we hope others understand, that in this there is a harmony between knowledge in the sense of science, that specialized and general knowledge which it is our purpose to uncover, and the community of man. We, like all men, are among those who bring a little light to the vast unending darkness of man's life and world. For us as for all men, change and eternity, specialization and unity, instrument and final purpose, community and individual man alone, complementary each to the other, both require and define our bonds and our freedom.

NOTE

The six chapters of this book are the Reith Lectures given over the home service of the British Broadcasting Corporation in November and December, 1953. They are printed essentially as broadcast. I have added two appendixes.

In the one I have collected the texts from which brief quotation is made in the lectures. The texts seem to me of interest in themselves; and in any case, this is the surest way to correct any distortion or color which my abbreviation may have introduced. In some cases the texts may even prompt curiosity to read further.

In the second appendix, I have given a brief and informal bibliography on atomic theory and its interpretation.

J. R. O.

APPENDIX I

SIR ISAAC NEWTON

(Page 12)

All these things being consider'd, it seems probable to me, that God in the Beginning form'd Matter in solid, massy, hard, impenetrable, moveable Particles, of such Sizes and Figures, and with such other Properties, and in such Proportion to Space, as most conduced to the End for which he form'd them; and that these primitive Particles being Solids, are incomparably harder than any porous Bodies compounded of them; even so very hard, as never to wear or break in pieces; no ordinary Power being able to divide what God himself made one in the first Creation. While the Particles continue entire, they may compose Bodies of one and the same Nature and Texture in all Ages: But should they wear away, or break in pieces, the Nature of Things depending on them, would be changed. Water and Earth, composed of old worn Particles and Fragments of Particles, would not be of the same Nature and Texture now, with Water and Earth composed of entire Particles in the Beginning. And therefore, that Nature may be lasting, the Changes of corporeal Things are to be placed only in the various Separations and new Associations and Motions of these permanent Particles; compound Bodies being apt to break, not in the midst of solid Particles, but where those Particles are laid together, and only touch in a few Points.

It seems to me farther, that these Particles have not only a *Vis inertæ*, accompanied with such passive Laws of Motion as naturally result from that Force, but also that they are moved by certain active Principles, such as is that of Gravity, and that which causes Fermentation, and the Cohesion of Bodies. These Principles I consider, not as occult Qualities, supposed to result from the specifick Forms of Things, but as general Laws of Nature, by which the Things themselves are form'd; their Truth appearing to us by Phænomena, though their Causes be not yet discover'd. . . .

Sir Isaac Newton, *Opticks* (New York: Dover Publications, Inc., 1952), Book 3, Part I, Query 31, p. 400. Based on the Fourth Edition, London, 1730.

THOMAS SPRAT

(Page 16)

I will here, in the first place, contract into few Words, the whole *Sum* of their *Resolutions;* which I shall often have occasion to touch upon in *Parcels.* Their Purpose is, in short, to make faithful *Records* of all the Works of *Nature,* or *Art,* which can come within their Reach; that so the present Age, and Posterity, may be able to put a Mark on the Errors, which have been strengthned by long Prescription; to restore the Truths, that have lain neglected; to push on those, which are already known, to more various Uses; and to make the way more passable, to what remains unreveal'd. This is the Compass of their Design. And to accomplish this, they have endeavour'd, to separate the Knowledge of *Nature,* from the Colours *Rhetorick,* the Devices of *Fancy,* or the delightful Deceit of *Fables.* They have labor'd to inlarge it, from being confin'd to the Custody of a few, or from Servitude to private Interests. They have striven to preserve it from being over-press'd by a confus'd Heap of vain and useless Particulars; or from being streightned and bound too much up by general

Doctrines. They have tried to put it into a Condition of perpetual Increasing; by settling an inviolable Correspondence between the Hand and the Brain. They have studied, to make it not only an Enterprise of one Season, or of some lucky Opportunity; but a Business of Time; a steady, a lasting, a popular, an uninterrupted Work. They have attempted, to free it from the Artifice, and Humors, and Passions of Sects; to render it an Instrument, whereby Mankind may obtain a Dominion over *Things,* and not only over one another's *Judgments:* And lastly, they have begun to establish these Reformations in Philosophy, not so much, by any solemnity of Laws, or Ostentation of Ceremonies, as by solid Practice and Examples; not by a glorious Pomp of Words; but by the silent, effectual, and unanswerable Arguments of real Productions.

This will more fully appear, by what I am to say on these four Particulars, which shall make up this Part of my Relation, the *Qualifications* of their *Members;* the *Manner* of their *Inquiry;* their *Weekly Assemblies;* and their *Way* of *Registring.*

As for what belongs to the *Members* themselves that are to constitute the *Society:* It is to be noted, that they have freely admitted Men of different Religions, Countries, and Professions of Life. This they were oblig'd to do, or else they would come far short of the Largeness of their own Declarations. For they openly profess, not to lay the Foundation of an *English, Scotch, Irish, Popish,* or *Protestant* Philosophy; but a Philosophy of *Mankind.*

That the *Church of England* ought not to be apprehensive of this free Converse of various Judgments, I shall afterwards manifest at large. For the present, I shall frankly assert, that our *Doctrine,* and *Discipline,* will be so far from receiving Damage by it; that it were the best Way to make them universally embrac'd, if they were oftner brought to be canvass'd amidst all Sorts of Dissenters. It is dishonorable, to pass a hard Censure on the Religions of all other Countries: It concerns them, to look to the Reasonableness of their Faith; and it is sufficient for us, to be establish'd in the Truth of our own.

Thomas Sprat, *The History of the Royal Society of London* (3rd ed.; London, 1722), pp. 61–63.

THOMAS JEFFERSON

(Page 18)

Monticello June 18. 99.

DEAR SIR,

I have to acknolege the reciept of your favor of May 14.
in which you mention that you have finished the 6. first books
of Euclid, plane trigonometry, surveying and algebra and
ask whether I think a further pursuit of that branch of science
would be useful to you. There are some propositions in the
latter books of Euclid, and some of Archimedes, which are
useful, and I have no doubt you have been made acquainted
with them. Trigonometry, so far as this, is most valuable to
every man, there is scarcely a day in which he will not resort
to it for some of the purposes of common life; the science of
calculation also is indispensible as far as the extraction of
the square and cube roots; Algebra as far as the quadratic
equation and the use of logarithms are often of value in ordinary cases: but all beyond these is but a luxury; a delicious
luxury indeed; but not to be indulged in by one who is to
have a profession to follow for his subsistence. In this light

I view the conic sections, curves of the higher orders, perhaps even spherical trigonometry, Algebraical operations beyond the 2d dimension, and fluxions. There are other branches of science however worth the attention of every man: Astronomy, botany, chemistry, natural philosophy, natural history, anatomy. Not indeed to be a proficient in them; but to possess their general principles and outlines, so as that we may be able to amuse and inform ourselves further in any of them as we proceed through life and have occasion for them. Some knowlege of them is necessary for our character as well as comfort. The general elements of astronomy and of natural philosophy are best acquired at an academy where we can have the benefit of the instruments and apparatus usually provided there: but the others may well be acquired from books alone as far as our purposes require. I have indulged myself in these observations to you, because the evidence cannot be unuseful to you of a person who has often had occasion to consider which of his acquisitions in science have been really useful to him in life, and which of them have been merely a matter of luxury.

I am among those who think well of the human character generally. I consider man as formed for society, and endowed by nature with those dispositions which fit him for society. I believe also, with Condorcet, as mentioned in your letter, that his mind is perfectible to a degree of which we cannot as yet form any conception. It is impossible for a man who takes a survey of what is already known, not to see what an immensity in every branch of science yet remains to be discovered, and that too of articles to which our faculties seem adequate. In geometry and calculation we know a great deal. Yet there are some desiderata. In anatomy great progress has been made; but much is still to be acquired. In natural history we possess knowlege; but we want a great deal. In chemistry we are not yet sure of the first elements. Our natural philosophy is in a very infantine state; perhaps for great advances in it, a further progress in chemistry is necessary. Surgery is well advanced; but prodigiously short of what may be. The state of medecine is worse than that of total ignorance. Could we divest ourselves of every thing we suppose we know in it, we should start from a higher ground and with fairer prospects. From Hippocrates to Brown we have had nothing but a succession of hypothetical systems each having it's day of vogue, like the fashions and fancies of caps and gowns, and yielding in turn to the next caprice. Yet the human frame, which is to be the subject of suffering and torture under these learned modes, does not change. We have a few medecines, as the bark, opium, mercury, which in a few well defined diseases are of unquestionable virtue: but the residuary list of the materia medica, long as it is, contains but the charlataneries of the art; and of the diseases of doubtful form, physicians have ever had a false knowlege, worse than ignorance. Yet surely the list of unequivocal diseases and remedies is capable of enlargement; and it is still more certain that in the other branches of science, great fields are yet to be explored to which our faculties are equal, and that to an extent of which we cannot fix the limits. I join you therefore in branding as cowardly the idea that the human mind is incapable of further advances. This is precisely the doctrine which the present despots of the earth are inculcating, and their friends here re-echoing; and applying especially to religion and politics; 'that it is not probable that any thing better will be discovered than what was known to our fathers.'

We are to look backwards then and not forwards for the improvement of science, and to find it amidst feudal barbarisms and the fires of Spital-fields. But thank heaven the American mind is already too much opened, to listen to these impostures; and while the art of printing is left to us, science can never be retrograde; what is once acquired of real knowlege can never be lost. To preserve the freedom of the human mind then and freedom of the press, every spirit should be ready to devote itself to martyrdom; for as long as we may think as we will, and speak as we think, the condition of man will proceed in improvement. The generation which is going off the stage has deserved well of mankind for the struggles it has made, and for having arrested that course of despotism which had overwhelmed the world for thousands and thousands of years. If there seems to be danger that the ground they have gained will be lost again, that danger comes from the generation your cotemporary. But that the enthusiasm which characterises youth should lift it's parracide hands against freedom and science would be such a monstrous phaenomenon as I cannot place among possible things in this age and this country. Your college at least has shewn itself incapable of it; and if the youth of any other place have seemed to rally under other banners it has been from delusions which they will soon dissipate. I shall be happy to hear from you from time to time, and of your progress in study, and to be useful to you in whatever is in my power; being with sincere esteem Dear Sir

Your friend & servt
Th: Jefferson

Scripta Mathematica, I (1932), 88–90.

THOMAS HOBBES

(Page 21)

Good successe is Power; because it maketh reputation of Wisdome, or good fortune; which makes men either feare him, or rely on him.

Affability of men already in power, is encrease of Power; because it gaineth love.

Reputation of Prudence in the conduct of Peace or War, is Power; because to prudent men, we commit the government of our selves, more willingly than to others.

Nobility is Power, not in all places, but onely in those Common-Wealths, where it has Priviledges: for in such priviledges consisteth their Power.

Eloquence is power; because it is seeming Prudence.

Forme is Power; because being a promise of Good, it recommendeth men to the favour of women and strangers.

The Sciences, are small Power; because not eminent; and therefore, not acknowledged in any man; nor are at all, but in a few; and in them, but of a few things. For Science is of that nature, as none can understand it to be, but such as in a good measure have attayned it.

Arts of publique use, as Fortification, making of Engines, and other Instruments of War; because they conferre to Defence, and Victory, are Power: And though the true Mother of them, be Science, namely the Mathematiques; yet, because they are brought into the Light, by the hand of the Artificer, they be esteemed (the Midwife passing with the vulgar for the Mother,) as his issue.

Thomas Hobbes, *Leviathan*, ed. by A. R. Waller ("Cambridge English Classics"; Cambridge: Cambridge University Press, 1904), Part I, Chap. 10, pp. 54–55.

INSCRIPTION ON STEEPLE KNOB OF ST. MARGARET'S CHURCH AT GOTHA

(Page 68)

Unsere Tage füllten den glücklichsten Zeitraum des achtzehnten Jahrhunderts. Kaiser, Könige, Fürsten steigen von ihrer gefürchteten Höhe menschenfreundlich herab, verachten Pracht und Schimmer, werden Väter, Freunde und Vertraute ihres Volks. Die Religion zerreisst das Pfaffengewand und tritt in ihrer Göttlichkeit hervor. Aufklärung geht mit Riesenschritten. Tausende unserer Brüder und Schwestern, die in geheiligter Unthätigkeit lebten, werden dem Staat geschenkt. Glaubenshass und Gewissenszwang sinken dahin; Menschenliebe und Freiheit im Denken gewinnen die Oberhand. Künste und Wissenschaften blühen, und tief dringen unsere Blicke in die Werkstatt der Natur. Handwerker nähern sich gleich den Künstlern der Vollkommenheit, nützliche Kenntnisse Keimen in allen Ständen. Hier habt Ihr eine getreue Schilderung unserer Zeit. Blickt nicht stolz auf uns herab, wenn Ihr höher steht und weiter seht als wir; erkennt vielmehr aus dem gegebenen Gemälde, wie sehr wir mit Muth und Kraft Euren Standort emporhoben und stützten. Thut für Eure Nachkommenschaft ein Gleiches und seid glücklich!

Our days have been the happiest time of the eighteenth century. Emperors, kings and princes step down from their feared heights, and as friends of men scorn pomp and glitter and become fathers, friends and confidants of their people. Religion tears off its popish garb and stands forth in its divinity. Enlightenment advances with giant steps. Thousands of our brothers and sisters who previously spent their lives in holied idleness are given back to the community. Hatred born of dogma and the compulsion of conscience sink away; love of man and freedom of thought gain the upper hand. The arts and sciences blossom, and our vision into the workshop of nature goes deep. Artisans approach artists in perfection; useful skills flower at all levels. Here you have a faithful portrait of our time. Look not proudly down upon us, should you stand higher or see farther than we, but rather recognize from this picture how with courage and strength we raised and supported your standard. Do the same for those who come after you and rejoice!

Hermann Hettner, *Literaturgeschichte des Achtzehnten Jahrhunderts,* Vol. III (Braunschweig: Friederich Vieweg und Sohn, 1879), Book 2, Chap. 1, p. 171.

ALEXIS DE TOCQUEVILLE

(Page 92)

DE L'USAGE QUE LES AMÉRICAINS FONT DE L'ASSOCIATION DANS LA VIE CIVILE

Je ne veux point parler de ces associations politiques à l'aide desquelles les hommes cherchent à se défendre contre l'action despotique d'une majorité ou contre les empiétements du pouvoir royal. J'ai déjà traité ce sujet ailleurs. Il est clair que si chaque citoyen, à mesure qu'il devient individuellement plus faible, et par conséquent plus incapable de préserver isolément sa liberté, n'apprenait pas l'art de s'unir à ses semblables pour la défendre, la tyrannie croîtrait nécessairement avec l'égalité. Il ne s'agit ici que des associations qui se forment dans la vie civile, et dont l'objet n'a rien de politique.

Les associations politiques qui existent aux États-Unis ne forment qu'un détail au milieu de l'immense tableau que l'ensemble des associations y présente.

Les Américains de tous les âges, de toutes les conditions, de tous les esprits, s'unissent sans cesse. Non-seulement ils ont des associations commerciales et industrielles auxquelles tous prennent part, mais ils en ont encore de mille autres espèces: de religieuses, de morales, de graves, de futiles, de fort générales et de très-particulières, d'immenses et de fort petites; les Américains s'associent pour donner des fêtes, fonder des séminaires, bâtir des auberges, élever des églises, répandre des livres, envoyer des missionaires aux antipodes; ils créent de cette manière des hôpitaux, des prisons, des écoles. S'agit-il enfin de mettre en lumière une vérité, ou de développer un sentiment par l'appui d'un grand exemple: ils s'associent. Partout où, à la tête d'une entreprise nouvelle, vous voyez en France le gouvernement, et en Angleterre un grand seigneur, comptez que vous apercevrez aux États-Unis une association.

J'ai rencontré en Amérique des sortes d'associations dont je confesse que je n'avais pas même l'idée, et j'ai souvent admiré l'art infini avec lequel les habitants des États-Unis parvenaient à fixer un but commun aux efforts d'un grand nombre d'hommes, et à les faire marcher librement.

OF THE USE WHICH THE AMERICANS MAKE OF PUBLIC ASSOCIATIONS IN CIVIL LIFE

I do not propose to speak of those political associations by the aid of which men endeavor to defend themselves against the despotic action of a majority or against the aggressions of regal power. That subject I have already treated. If each citizen did not learn, in proportion as he individually becomes more feeble and consequently more incapable of preserving his freedom singlehanded, to combine with his fellow citizens for the purpose of defending it, it is clear that tyranny would unavoidably increase together with equality.

Only those associations that are formed in civil life without reference to political objects are here referred to. The political associations that exist in the United States are only a single feature in the midst of the immense assemblage of asso-

ciations in that country. Americans of all ages, all conditions, and all dispositions constantly form associations. They have not only commercial and manufacturing companies, in which all take part, but associations of a thousand other kinds, religious, moral, serious, futile, general or restricted, enormous or diminutive. The Americans make associations to give entertainments, to found seminaries, to build inns, to construct churches, to diffuse books, to send missionaries to the antipodes; in this manner they found hospitals, prisons, and schools. If it is proposed to inculcate some truth or to foster some feeling by the encouragement of a great example, they form a society. Wherever at the head of some new undertaking you see the government in France, or a man of rank in England, in the United States you will be sure to find an association.

I met with several kinds of associations in America of which I confess I had no previous notion; and I have often admired the extreme skill with which the inhabitants of the United States succeed in proposing a common object for the exertions of a great many men and in inducing them voluntarily to pursue it.

Alexis de Tocqueville, *De la Démocratie en Amérique*, Vol. III (14ième édition; Paris: Michel Levy Frères, 1864), Deuxième Partie, Chap. 2, p. 175. *English translation from* Alexis de Tocqueville, *Democracy in America*, Vol. II (New York: Alfred A. Knopf, 1948), Book 2, Chap. 5, p. 106.

APPENDIX II

Chapters Two to Five deal at some length with atomic theory and with some of the experiments that underlie it. With the exception of contemporary work on the "new particles," there are many admirable technical text books and monographs.

As for Chapter Two, the interested reader may wish to turn to the classic texts of E. R. Rutherford, *Radioactive Substances and their Radiations* (Cambridge: Cambridge University Press; New York: Putnam; 1913), and to Rutherford, Chadwick, and Ellis, *Radiations from Radioactive Substances* (Cambridge: Cambridge University Press, 1930). The "new particles" were discussed at a conference held at Bagnères de Bigorre, July, 1953. The record of this conference, issued by the École Polytechnique, Paris, gives a most vivid impression of the present state of knowledge, ignorance, and progress. Even for those who do not wish to consult the proceedings of the conference, the comment following the title may be of interest: *"Les particules décrites au cours de ce Congrès ne sont pas entièrement fictives, et toute analogie avec des particules existant dans la nature n'est pas une pure coïncidence."*

There are numerous good technical texts on the quantum mechanics, the quantum theory of atoms. In particular I recommend:

P. A. M. Dirac. *The Principles of Quantum Mechanics.* Oxford: Clarendon Press, 1930.

W. Pauli. "Die Allgemeinen Prinzipien der Wellenmechanik," *Handbuch der Physik,* XXIV (1933), *1,* 83.

L. I. Schiff. *Quantum Mechanics.* New York: McGraw-Hill Book Co., 1949.

Of these, Schiff's text is the most elementary.

No attempt has been made in the lectures to give a full historic account of the contributions made to the development of quantum theory. Where names have been mentioned, it is because they have become generally identified with principles or with theories; but any account of the history of quantum theory should at least mention Born, Dirac, and Pauli, in addition to the names that occur in the text.

As to the interpretation of quantum theory, these may serve to guide the reader should he want more detailed, more original, and more substantive accounts of the matters touched on in the lectures:

W. Heisenberg. *The Physical Principles of the Quantum Theory.* Chicago: University of Chicago Press, 1930.

N. Bohr. *Atomic Theory and the Description of Nature.* New York: (Cambridge University Press) The Macmillan Co., 1934.

N. Bohr. "On the Notions of Causality and Complementarity," *Dialectica,* II (1948), 312.

N. Bohr. "Discussion with Einstein on Epistemological Problems in Atomic Physics," *Albert Einstein, Philosopher-Scientist.* Edited by P. A. Schilpp. "Library of Living Philosophers"; Evanston, Illinois, 1949.

W. Pauli. *"Die philosophische Bedeutung der Idee der Komplementarität," Experientia,* VI (1950), 72.

ABOUT THE AUTHOR

J. ROBERT OPPENHEIMER *has been director of the Institute for Advanced Study at Princeton, New Jersey, since 1947. He is a physicist trained at Harvard, Cambridge and Göttingen, who has been a professor at the University of California and at the California Institute of Technology. Between 1943 and 1945 he was director of the laboratory at Los Alamos in New Mexico, where the first atomic bombs were made.*